DEFORESTATION IN UGANDA

DEFORESTATION IN UGANDA

C.A. Hamilton

1984
OXFORD UNIVERSITY PRESS
Nairobi

Oxford University Press

OXFORD LONDON GLASGOW
NEW YORK TORONTO MELBOURNE AUCKLAND
NAIROBI DAR ES SALAAM CAPE TOWN
KUALA LUMPUR SINGAPORE HONG KONG TOKYO
DELHI BOMBAY CALCUTTA MADRAS KARACHI

and associates in
BEIRUT BERLIN IBADAN MEXICO CITY NICOSIA

ISBN 0 19 572547 6

© Oxford University Press 1984

OXFORD is a trademark of Oxford University Press

Published by Oxford University Press, East and Central Africa,
Science House, Monrovia Street, P.O. Box 72532, Nairobi, and
printed by Acme Press (K) Ltd., Mfangano Street, P.O. Box 40497,
Nairobi, Kenya.

Contents

Acknowledgements

I am indebted to the Forest Department, Uganda, for asking me to study the problem of deforestation in Uganda. Officers of the department have invariably proved to be courteous and helpful and I extend to all of them my deepest gratitude. Also in Uganda, staff of the Departments of Botany and Forestry at Makerere University have given me their support in this study. A special word of thanks is due to the students of botany who carried out the surveys mentioned in this work.

The Director and other members of the Regional Remote Sensing Facility in Nairobi went out of their way to make available to me the use of their facilities, including the gift of a number of LANDSAT photographs.

Finally, I am very grateful to the East African Wildlife Society for providing the financial backing without which this book could not have been produced.

Plates

(Between pages 24 and 25)

1. LANDSAT image of Mt Elgon and vicinity
2. LANDSAT image of eastern Buganda and southern Busoga
3. LANDSAT image of Kampala and neighbourhood
4. LANDSAT image of south-western Uganda
5. LANDSAT image of the eastern part of Lake Albert and adjoining country
6. The canopy tree *Newtonia buchananii*, showing buttresses
7. The canopy tree *Ficus mucosa* in Mpanga Forest, near Kampala
8. View of the canopy of swamp-edge forest near Entebbe, showing *Musanga cecropioides* and *Raphia farinifera*
9. Bwindi Forest, Kabale District
10. Clearing forest for farmland in Kabale District
11. Mechanical logging in Budongo Forest
12. Devastation in Budongo Forest following mechanical logging
13. *Loudetia* grassland near Entebbe, with forest thickets, showing *Maesopsis eminii*
14. Intensively farmed slopes on the western side of Mt Elgon
15. Agricultural land in Kabale District, with the Bufumbira Volcanoes
16. The Lake Bunyonyi area of Kabale District
17. Newly opened agricultural land near Rugege Forest, Rwanda
18. Private nursery near Kampala, growing *Eucalyptus* and cypress
19. Taro and maize growing on a reclaimed papyrus swamp near Kampala

List of figures

List of tables

Chapter 1

The deforestation problem
in Uganda

Uganda is an agricultural country with few proven mineral reserves and little prospect of rapid industrial development; as in the past, agriculture and forestry will continue to play important roles in the economy. It is thus of considerable concern that the tree resources of the country are being rapidly depleted, leading to an increasing shortage of firewood and other wood products as well as general environmental degradation.

It has been the opinion of many Ugandans and visitors from other countries that Uganda is a bountiful land, with the potential to offer a good standard of living to every one of its inhabitants. Certainly it is blessed with a climate which is the envy of many other African states. The fact that the standard of living of the average Ugandan has declined over the past few years is sometimes regarded as an aberrant and temporary phenomenon caused largely by political instability. According to those who hold this view, once the political problems have been 'sorted out', Uganda will resume an upward trend in economic development to become once again the 'Pearl of Africa'.

The economic health of Uganda will undoubtedly be greatly influenced by the ways in which the natural resources of the country are exploited. Uganda is relatively poor in minerals and her primary natural resource is land, yielding crops and trees which, unlike minerals, are potentially renewable. With careful management and long-term planning, agricultural and forestry productivity can be maintained or even increased. However, the land may also be exploited destructively, possibly in ways which appear to be initially successful and which yield high profits in the short term, but which eventually result in environmental deterioration seriously undermining future potential.

Virtually all economists stress the vital central position of agriculture in Uganda's development (e.g. Nsibambi and Katorobo 1981), but it is often overlooked that in the Ugandan context forestry is also vital for future prosperity. Forests serve a number of protective roles, helping to maintain soil fertility, prevent soil erosion, and provide a reliable water supply. Additionally, there are theoretical reasons to suggest that a good covering of forests helps to maintain a relatively moist climate. Furthermore, it is not only forests as such that produce these benefits. Trees or small plantations scattered through agricultural and grazing land can also protect the environment and their protection and establishment should be given much more prominence in schemes of rural development than has been the case in the past.

In addition to their various protective functions, trees play more direct roles in the economy. Their main uses are as unsawn round timber for building, poles, and fencing, as sawn timber for construction and furniture, and as fuel, which, in terms of the volume of wood harvested, is the most important of all. Wood is believed to provide over 90% of the total fuel used in Uganda at the present time.

Unfortunately, Uganda is expected to be unable to avoid a number of potentially disastrous trends which are taking place in man's use of resources throughout tropical Africa and which are leading to an accelerating decline in the productivity of the land. These problems are evident in the increasing tendency for the food production of African countries to fall short of the levels necessary to support their people. The causes of these problems are a complex of environmental, economic, and political factors, some of which require concerted international effort for their alleviation and lie beyond the scope of this work. On the other hand there are actions that Ugandans could take which would go a long way towards the solution of these problems.

The population of Uganda is increasing rapidly and, as it does so, so too does the demand for products from the land. To maintain current living standards, a doubling in population means essentially a doubling in the amount of food that needs to be grown, a doubling in the amount of wood required as fuel, and so on. There is no doubt that Uganda could accommodate many more people than it does today, and indeed even provide them with a high standard of living, if its external economy was radically different from that which actually prevails. Thus, if Uganda could afford to import large quantities of, say, food and wood, then it could support a higher population. However, such a revolution is most improbable in the foreseeable future and there is every likelihood that the welfare of Uganda will continue to depend, as it has in the past, primarily on the ways in which the natural resources present within its borders are utilized.

The size of a population that can be sustained on a permanent basis in a given area is dependent in part on the methods of land management

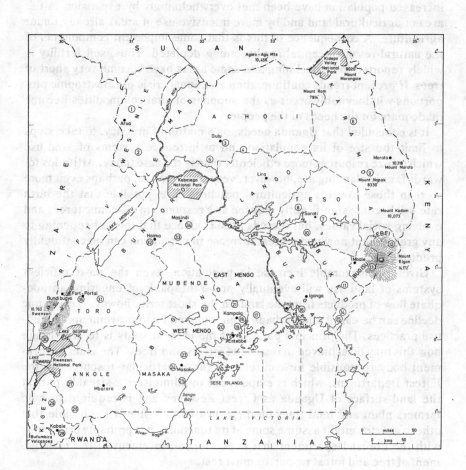

Figure 1. Uganda

The numbers show the locations of the homes of the 35 students who participated in the questionnaire survey discussed in Chapter 3. Note that the Districts (e.g. Acholi) have recently been renamed after prominent towns, but the old names are used here to facilitate reference to the literature.

employed. In Uganda, systems of cultivation of food crops and of stock keeping have proved rather conservative and the demands made by the increased population have been met overwhelmingly by expansion in the area of agricultural land and by more intensive use of areas already under agriculture. A consequence of this is that some important components of the natural-resource capital are becoming depleted. Thus, soil fertility is widely reported to be declining and some areas have become very short of trees. If present trends continue, then a national crisis of catastrophic proportions will inevitably occur as the supplies of vital commodities become inadequate for the needs of the people.

It is concluded that Uganda needs, as a matter of urgency, to take steps to limit the size of its population and to introduce systems of land use which utilize resources more efficiently than is the case today. Attitudes towards family planning are, however, very conservative, perhaps even more so than those towards agricultural practices. It is possible that the birth rate will become significantly reduced as a response to economic forces and evolving social values, but there is little evidence that this is happening to any great extent now and a great increase in population can be confidently predicted.

Given an inexorable increase in population, even the most efficient systems of land use will eventually prove incapable of ensuring an adequate flow of products from the land. In the short term, however, economic decline can be eased and perhaps even reversed by improvements in land-use practices. The principal purpose of the present study is to investigate how this may be achieved in respect of forests and trees. The main government body responsible for control over these particular resources is the Forest Department, which is empowered to administer a sizeable part of the land-surface of Uganda as Forest Reserves and is required to help farmers plant and tend trees on their own land. While it is possible that other agencies might assume some of its functions, it is probably principally with the Forest Department that hopes for improvement in the management of tree and forest resources must rest.

The Forest Department was founded in its present form in 1929, and during the next forty years of its existence it gradually developed efficient techniques for the sustained supply of tree products, both from natural forests and from plantations of mainly exotic trees. Unfortunately, during the last ten to fifteen years methods of forest management once well established have tended to become ineffective. This has resulted in the loss of an unknown, but certainly very substantial, area of the forest-reserve estate by illegal agricultural encroachment, a huge increase in the unlicensed exploitation of forest produce, and a virtually total failure of the Department to anticipate and meet shortages of fuel and other tree products. There have been parallel problems in other environmental agencies, and the overall result is that in parts of the country deterioration of the natural environment has reached crisis proportions. The well known recent human tragedy in Karamoja, involving many thousands of deaths through starvation, is due largely to ecological degradation at the hands of man. It can be predicted that problems of a similar magnitude will soon appear elsewhere, unless the efficiency with which natural resources are managed is radically improved.

Chapter 2

The Ugandan background

The most important common characteristic of all rain-forest soils [is] their low
content of plant nutrients. The leached and impoverished soils of the wet tropics
bear magnificent forest. . . . In the rain forest the vegetation itself sets up processes tending to counteract soil impoverishment and under undisturbed conditions there is a closed cycle of plant nutrients. . . . The existence of this closed
cycle makes it easy to understand why a soil bearing magnificent rain forest may
prove to be far from fertile when the land is cleared and cultivated. When the
forest is felled the capital of nutrients is removed or set free in the soil and the
humus layer is often destroyed at the same time by burning and exposure to the
sun. . . . Crops planted where rain forest has been cleared may do very well for a
few seasons, benefiting from the temporary enrichment of the soil, but before
long, unless special measures are taken, a sterile, uncultivable soil may develop.
(Richards 1979)

Forests and trees form part of the natural environment and a broad perspective is useful for appreciating how they contribute to the life of the
nation. Accordingly, a thumbnail sketch of the Ugandan environment is
given here to provide a context for subsequent discussion. This chapter is
based mainly on published information, nearly all of which dates from the
1960s or earlier. An attempt is made in Chapter 3 to assess how the environment has changed over the last 15 years.

Uganda is a rather small landlocked country straddling the Equator in
central Africa. Its total area of 236 000 km² is composed of 194 000 km² of
land and the notably high figure of 42 000 km² of open water and swamp.
Much of the country, including all the centre, lies at altitudes between
about 900 and 1500 m. Towards the south, near Lake Victoria, the characteristic scenery consists of flat-topped hills and broad intervening valleys
frequently containing swamps; towards the north, the landscape is more
subdued, consisting of gently rolling plains interrupted by occasional
mountains, hills, and inselbergs. The Rift Valley, which runs near the
western border, is represented by two troughs, that of Lakes Edward and
George at an altitude of about 900 m in the south, and that of Lake Albert at

an altitude of about 600 m in the north. Between these depressions lies the Rwenzori Range, rising to the highest peak in Uganda at 5110 m.

There are a number of volcanic centres associated with the Rift Valley. The most spectacular of these is in the extreme south-west and extends into neighbouring parts of Rwanda and Zaire; this centre includes the three quiescent Bufumbira Volcanoes of Muhavura (4130 m), Mgahinga (3470 m) and Sabinio (3630 m). The formation of the Rift Valley, an event which is believed to have occurred during the last 30 million years, was associated with the uplift of land in places along its margins, and today there is a chain of hills running along the eastern side of the Rift. Some of the more extensive blocks of forest are found on this belt of elevated land, which reaches a maximum altitude of 2500 m in Kigezi District in the south.

The main topographical features in northern Uganda lie towards the eastern and north-eastern borders and include four large Miocene volcanoes, Elgon (4320 m), Moroto (3080 m), Kadam (3070 m), and Napak (2540 m), and a number of hills and mountains composed of basement rocks, such as the Agoro-Agu Mountains (2850 m), the Morongole Mountains (2750 m), and Mt Rom (2320 m).

Uganda is a country of considerable climatic variation, with important consequences for the distribution of vegetation and land use. According to the *Atlas of Uganda* (Department of Lands and Surveys 1962) much of the country receives between 1015 mm (40″) and 1525 mm (60″) of precipitation in an average year. Mountains, however, tend to be wetter, with Rwenzori, the Bufumbira Volcanoes and the southern and western slopes of Mt Elgon being particularly moist. The Sese Islands in Lake Victoria, with over 2030 mm (80″) of rain, are also very wet, and there is a narrow zone with relatively high precipitation on the mainland close to the lake shore. The driest district of Uganda is Karamoja, with rainfall declining from about 1015 mm (40″) in the west to less than 510 mm (20″) in the north-east. Other areas of Uganda which receive less than 1015 mm (40″) are parts of the Edward-George and Albert troughs and a wedge of land on the border between Ankole and Buganda.

In addition to the mean annual total, other aspects of rainfall are important, particularly seasonal distribution and reliability from year to year. Regarding distribution, the south of the country has two rainy seasons, one in April-May and another in October-November, while the north has only a single rainy season, the wettest month being July. The reliability of rainfall declines towards the north. The importance of distribution can be gauged by a comparison of the climate and vegetation of Gulu in the north and Kampala in the south. The *Atlas of Uganda* shows the mean annual rainfall at Gulu to be higher than that at Kampala and therefore it may seem surprising that Gulu is situated in the savanna zone and Kampala in the forest zone. The explanation is that precipitation at Gulu tends to be concentrated into a single season, the dry season being long and having little rain, while at Kampala there are two rainy seasons and the intervening dry seasons are less severe.

Variations in mean temperature are related principally to altitude and, since temperature is one of the main determinants of evaporation, the water balance tends to become more favourable for plant growth at higher altitudes. This is one of the reasons why forest was the original natural vegetation on mountains even in Karamoja, the driest district in the country.

The characteristics of soil, like those of climate, exert major influences on vegetation and land use in Uganda. Soil properties are determined by a number of factors, including climate, parent material, topography, plant and animal influences, and land use, and soil variation occurs on several quite different geographical scales. On the smallest scale, there can often be striking variations related to such factors as the former positions of house sites, anthills, cattle compounds, bonfires, and tree stumps (Chenery 1960; Eggeling 1948a). On the intermediate scale, there is major variation associated with topography, the soils of hilltops tending to differ from those of midslopes and both of these contrasting markedly with those of valley bottoms. The concept of the 'catena', a term which originated in Uganda (Milne 1935), is valuable for describing this variation, the catena being one unit of a repeated pattern of soil variation related to topography. Soil catenas are associated with parallel contrasts in vegetation and land use and should provide one of the fundamental planning bases for rural development. Parent material can also be an important determinant of soil type. Both volcanic rocks and base-rich basement-complex rocks weather to give soils well endowed with plant nutrients, but are of only local occurrence in Uganda; most soils are developed on acidic basement-complex rocks which yield few nutrients. Finally, on the largest scale, there is a tendency for particular soil types to be associated with major climatic zones. This is evident in the very wide distribution of ferralitic and, to a lesser degree, ferruginous soils in Uganda; each is developed on a variety of parent rocks. (Ferralitic and ferruginous soils are sometimes known, respectively, as oxisols and ultisols—they have many physical and chemical properties in common.)

According to the *Atlas of Uganda*, the ferralitic is the most widely distributed soil type, occurring in both forest and savanna zones. Its profile consists of a thin (20−35 cm) topsoil and a deep (often over 5 or even 10 m) subsoil. Organic matter and nutrients are strongly concentrated in the topsoil. The subsoil consists mainly of kaolinite clay and iron oxides, and contains few reserves of weatherable minerals. It may be noted that kaolinite clay has a low inherent ability to retain nutrients. Ferralitic soils are red or yellow in colour, and range in texture from clay loams to sandy loams; red clay loams tend to predominate in wetter districts and are reported to be relatively fertile, while in drier areas, such as northern Uganda, soils tend to be yellow, sandier, and to contain fewer nutrients.

Ferralitic soils can be productive, a characteristic attributable to the relatively high rainfall, considerable soil depth, and relatively nutrient-rich topsoil. It is vital to realize that soil fertility can be easily and rapidly diminished through erosion of the topsoil, and that, once lost, it is prohibitively expensive to restore. The input of plant nutrients into the soil body, either through rock weathering or by arrival in rain or dust from the atmosphere, proceeds at a rate which is much slower than that at which nutrients can be lost through bad management; for practical purposes the soil cover of Uganda should be regarded as an irreplaceable capital resource. Conservation of the topsoil and retention of soil depth are essential for a bright economic future for Uganda (Griffith 1950). In the words of the one-time chief soil surveyor of Uganda, once the topsoil "is lost by erosion fertility and productivity go for good" (Chenery 1960, p. 32). And so too, it must be added, do any prospects of national prosperity.

In view of the great capacity for loss of nutrients by leaching in a wet tropical climate, it is remarkable that the nutrients are concentrated in a thin horizon just beneath the surface of the ground, a long way above the parent rock out of which most of the nutrients presumably once weathered. The reason for this is that in both natural forest and natural savanna ecosystems in Uganda nutrients are tightly cycled between the vegetation and the topsoil and few are lost by leaching (Eggeling 1948a). Dead vegetation and animal remains are rapidly decomposed and the contained nutrients are quickly reabsorbed by plants.

Man has greatly modified natural soil-plant-animal systems nearly everywhere in Uganda. One important result of man's intervention has been almost always to speed up the rate of soil erosion, defined as the bodily removal of soil by such agencies as running water and wind. Erosion is encouraged by the disruption of the plant cover and the creation of areas of bare soil. According to Dunne (1979), who has made a quantitative study of erosion in Kenya, land use is the dominant controlling agent over the rate of erosion, with climate and topography of secondary importance. The amount of soil eroded from agricultural land is often more than 100 times greater than that from forest. Unfortunately, it is the topsoil with its concentration of nutrients which tends to be eroded first, and therefore erosion is serious, not only because of its effect on soil depth, but also because soil fertility can easily be greatly depleted. Although a problem everywhere, the rate of erosion is sometimes reduced in wet areas through the ability of plants to spread rapidly over the ground. The problem is regarded by the National Report (Government of Uganda 1972) as being most severe in Karamoja.

Acceleration of the rate of soil erosion is not the only way in which man's actions can deplete the store of soil nutrients. Burning is often to the short-term advantage of the farmer, in that it clears the ground of established unwanted vegetation, induces fresh grass growth (valuable for pasture management), and releases nutrients for immediate uptake by plants. But, if burning is repeated year after year on the same site, then the soil becomes steadily less fertile as its nutrients are lost through volatilization, wind dispersal of ash, and leaching. Burning also reduces the amount of soil organic matter; since the ability of a soil to retain nutrients is strongly influenced by its organic-matter content, this too is likely to result in a diminution of the nutrient store. A lowering of organic matter also means that nutrients added to the soil tend to be leached rapidly out of the rooting zone so that the addition of artificial fertilizers becomes an inefficient and costly process.

It should be clear from the foregoing that the natural fertility of Ugandan soils depends substantially on the protection afforded by the vegetation cover. Over most of the country the influence of man is so pervasive that there is much uncertainty about the appearance of the vegetation which existed prior to human influence. Nevertheless, reconstruction of the pattern of the original vegetation gives a valuable guide to land-use potential and can assist in agricultural and forestry planning. A map showing the reconstructed original vegetation of Uganda, excluding Kara-moja, was prepared by Langdale-Brown (1960). It shows that before the arrival of agriculture a considerable part of the land-surface was covered by forest and almost all the rest of the country was clothed by other types of tree-rich vegetation, either thicket or wooded savanna. Regarding Kara-moja, it is known that this is a region which has witnessed very major changes in vegetation during recent years and the nature of the original vegetation is particularly uncertain. However, Wilson (1962) has attempted a map of the vegetation in A.D. 1900 and this shows most of the district as woodland or tree-rich grassland; forest was restricted to the mountains, while succulent-rich steppe and other 'arid' vegetation types, which are extensive today, were then confined to a narrow zone close to the present Kenyan border. Trees are thus thought to have once been abundant almost everywhere in Karamoja, as in the rest of the country.

The distinctions between the various types of vegetation mentioned in the preceding paragraph will now be briefly discussed (see also Greenway 1943 and Lind and Morrison 1974).

Forest is a type of vegetation dominated by trees, many species of which are usually tall at maturity and have straight trunks. The canopy is typically deep, being composed of several layers of foliage, and the herbaceous vegetation is generally rather open and lacks the tussock-forming grasses which are so characteristic of many types of savanna. The area believed to have been covered by forest prior to the introduction of agriculture had three geographical components. One was a region roughly 80 km wide stretching inland from Lake Victoria; another ran down western Uganda, mainly along the high ground on the shoulder of the Rift; the third consisted of the scattered forests on mountains in all parts of the country. The first two regions were possibly linked to one another around Mubende. The distribution of this original forest cover was closely related to the availability of moisture. The first two regions formed part of areas with an annual precipitation in excess of 1015 mm (40″) and two rainfall peaks, and the third was associated with the more favourable moisture balance of higher altitudes.

In *wooded savanna*, trees are characteristically shorter than in forest and the canopy much less dense. Crowns of trees are sometimes in lateral contact, but they do not overlap and the trees in some types of woodland can be quite widely spaced. The herbaceous stratum is composed mainly of tussock grasses and today is regularly burnt by man. According to Langdale-Brown (1960) two types of wooded savanna were predominant in Uganda before the introduction of agriculture. These were Combretaceous Woodland and *Butryospermum* Woodland, the former tending to occur in wetter areas.

Thicket is characterized by a dense cover of shrubs and trees, many multistemmed.

Steppe is a term which Wilson (1962) has used to describe a range of vegetation types of low stature found in arid or heavily over-grazed areas; the proportion of woody plants to grasses is variable.

Current maps of the modern vegetation are based on a government survey carried out in the late 1950s (Langdale-Brown *et al.* 1964). Since then there have undoubtedly been large-scale, though largely undocumented, alterations in the vegetation of many areas. The distribution of forest according to the vegetation survey of the late 1950s is shown on Figure 2. An outstanding feature is the great extent to which the area of forest has been reduced over the years. Instead of forming great swathes sweeping across the country, forest today is found only as isolated islands in a sea of agricultural and savanna communities.

Very little is known about the dates of forest destruction, but it is believed that all except the driest forests were little influenced by man before the arrival of agriculture. Archaeological records suggest that cultivation started in Uganda between 400 and 300 B.C. (Phillipson 1977) and was

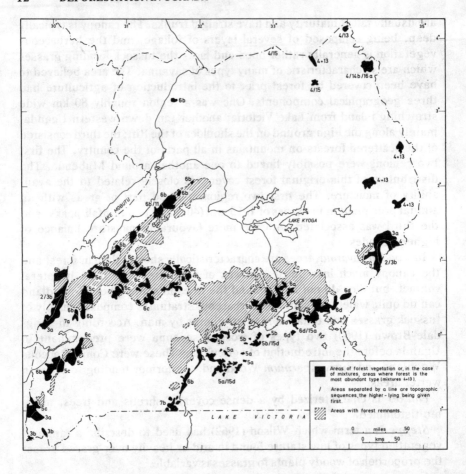

Figure 2. Forest vegetation of Uganda in the 1950s (Based on the map in the *Atlas of Uganda* (1962); numbers and names follow those in the Atlas.)

Key to forest and other vegetation types:

2.   Ericaceous Belt

3 & 4.   Montane Forest Belt

3a.   Moist Lower Montane Forest and Bamboo Zones

3b.   Upper Montane Forest Zone

4.   Dry Lower Montane Forest Zone

5.   Medium-Altitude Moist Evergreen Forest

5a.   *Piptadeniastrum-Uapaca*

5b.   *Piptadeniastrum-Albizzia-Celtis*

5c.   *Parinari*

6.   Medium-Altitude Moist Semi-deciduous Forest

6a.   *Celtis-Holoptelea*

6b.   *Celtis-Cynometra*

6c.   *Albizzia-Markhamia*

6d.   *Albizzia-Chlorophora*

7.   Swamp Forest

7a.   *Rauwolfia-Croton*

7b.   *Baikiaea-Podocarpus*

(Continued opposite)

accompanied by the first appearance of iron implements, which must have greatly facilitated forest clearance. Domestic animals, including cattle, were present in parts of Kenya and northern Tanzania somewhat earlier, and it is possible that pastoralism slightly predates cultivation in Uganda. Forest clearance is recorded in pollen diagrams from Kigezi (Morrison and Hamilton 1974), Rwenzori (Livingstone 1967) and more doubtfully Lake Victoria (Kendall 1969), but in none of these has the date of clearance been more than approximately established. Langdale-Brown (1960) has estimated the extent of forest in Uganda for three years during the present century, though unfortunately without giving details of the basis of his calculations. These estimates provide a rough picture of the rate of forest clearance (Table 1); there is an indication of an accelerating rate of forest destruction. It must be stressed that by no means all forest and tree destruction during the present century has been by smallholding farmers. Large numbers of trees have been uprooted in operations aimed at clearing tsetse flies or to create ranches, often to very dubious long-term advantage. Also, high concentrations of elephants, probably caused by agricultural pressure, were at one time a prime cause of massive tree death in Kabalega and Kidepo National Parks (Harrington and Ross 1974; Laws *et al.* 1970).

Table 1. Estimates of forest cover in Uganda, A.D. 1900 to 1958

Date (A.D.)	Area of forest and moist thicket (km²)	Percentage of forest and moist thicket[1]
1900	30 901	12.7
1926	26 277	10.8
1958	11 176	4.6

1. Percentages relate to the total area of Uganda

Source: Langdale-Brown (1960)

Although the spread of agriculture has destroyed most of the original forest cover, it would be mistaken to regard changes in vegetation during the agricultural period as occurring entirely in one direction. Extensive parts of some modern forests, such as Kasyoha-Kitomi, Mabira, and

---

(Key to forest and other vegetation types continued)

11. *Combretum* mixed savanna	15. Grass savanna
13. Mixed wooded savanna	15d. With *Loudetia* and *Eragrostis*
14b. Dry *Acacia* savanna with *Themeda*	16a. Semi-deciduous thicket

Maramagambo, are believed to be of secondary origin, not primeval (Philip 1962; Synnott 1971). A spectacular demonstration of the spread of forest is provided by the presence of massive earthworks, probably dating to c. A.D. 1400—1500, within Bugoma Forest; these earthworks are overgrown today by large trees with girths of up to 4.6 m (Osmaston 1959).

Epidemics of disease affecting man or his domestic animals are known to have caused massive local depopulation. Large parts of southern Busoga, including Buvuma Island, are covered by young forest which has grown up on land which was cultivated before the spread of sleeping sickness at the beginning of the twentieth century. Epidemics have been suggested as responsible for the large areas of colonizing forest in Kasyoha-Kitomi and Maramagambo (Synnott 1971). The considerable stretches of colonizing forest and thicket in Mubende District could have been due to depopulation during the ninteenth or twentieth centuries as a result of conflicts between the Kingdoms of Buganda and Bunyoro.

As we have seen, agriculture is the main economic activity in Uganda and will remain so for the foreseeable future. The majority of farmers are smallholders, living in scattered homesteads and using traditional agricultural techniques. The tools of the cultivator are generally limited to the hoe and the panga (machete). There are very few tractors, virtually no irrigation, and the employment of fertilizers and insecticides is minimal. Agriculture in Uganda is thus very closely tied to the natural environment, an immediate dependency which means that every effort should be made to maintain and if possible improve climatic and soil conditions suitable for agriculture. Unfortunately, the evidence suggests that the quality of both of these important resources is deteriorating, partly because of the continuing destruction of forests and trees.

Crops in Uganda are generally classified into export ('cash') and food crops. Coffee, which is by far the most important cash crop at present, is grown in wet, previously forested areas such as Buganda and Bugisu. With regard to food plants, virtually all the crops of the drier areas are annuals, such as grains and pulses; perennials, such as bananas, are only abundant in wetter regions. Mainly as a consequence of rainfall variation, the acreage cultivated per person in Lango and Acholi is nearly double that in Buganda (McMaster 1962).

Systems of cultivation for annual crops in Uganda traditionally include a period when fallow vegetation is allowed to spread over abandoned fields. The intention is to restore soil fertility, although the extent to which this actually happens depends on a large number of factors, including the nature of the soil and the kind of fallow vegetation which develops. As a very rough guide to the traditional pattern, the norm may be considered to be three years of crops followed by three years of fallow (McMaster

1962). Forest or other types of taller woody vegetation do not normally constitute part of the cycle. Extensive areas of secondary forest or colonizing thicket are due to catastrophic events disrupting normal agricultural activities.

Fallow vegetation varies from the lush to the sparse. Elephant grass, *Pennisetum purpureum*, a common colonizer in some wetter areas, is a well known restorer of soil fertility; the deep and extensive roots of this plant draw up nutrients and, in addition, rootlets penetrate intricately into the soil body, thereby improving drainage (Chenery 1960). This helps to counteract the downwash of fine soil particles through the soil profile during the crop phase; these particles can block soil pores and impede the movement of water. In some places the development of pioneer vegetation on abandoned land can be very slow because of soil degradation resulting from poor agricultural methods. This is illustrated on the Sese Islands where, in spite of plentiful rainfall, many old fields and pastures abandoned during a sleeping-sickness epidemic have been colonized only extremely slowly by forest (Eggeling 1948a; Thomas 1941).

Some people consider that there is plenty of land available in Uganda for future agricultural expansion, but this is certainly a false view if present methods of land use continue. Only a few regions, such as parts of Bunyoro and Mubende, are capable of absorbing more people with reasonable ease, but these areas have been targets for immigrants from less fortunate districts for some time and will soon in turn be overpopulated. According to McMaster (1962), even in 1958 extensive parts of Uganda were suffering from a shortage of good agricultural land, because the fallow phase of the agricultural cycle had been reduced to an unsatisfactory length or even completely eliminated. It was estimated that during 1958 13% of potentially cultivable land in Uganda was actually being cultivated (Department of Lands and Surveys 1962)—a figure which may seem low, but which hides major regional variation, from 1.3% in Karamoja to 71.3% in central Bugisu. It is not surprising that agricultural scientists at that time concluded that there was a serious land problem in Uganda. In the words of McMaster (1962), in many parts of Uganda 'methods [of agriculture] must improve, people must move, or the land must suffer.'

In parts of Uganda domestic animals, especially cattle, hold a significant place in the economy. With minor exceptions, the only processes used to manage pastures are periodic burning and the local migration of the herds. Within the limits imposed by tribal tolerance, there is virtually unregulated competition for the available grazing areas. Cattle assume special importance in parts of northern Uganda, both culturally and as modifiers of the environment. In Karamoja, for instance, cattle are a major cause of the massive vegetation changes which have occurred during the past eighty years (Eggeling 1948a; Thomas 1943; Wilson 1962). At the turn of the century much of Karamoja is believed to have carried woodland or wooded grassland and the grazing was rich; but, as the human and cattle populations increased, grass height became shorter, fires were less frequent, the number of trees was reduced, unpalatable thorn and succulent thicket spread, the amount of bare ground increased, and the soil became more compact and less pervious. As a result the rate of soil erosion greatly accelerated. The evidence of Wilson (1962), Eggeling (1948a), and modern satellite pictures indicates that the most seriously overgrazed areas are not necessarily those with the lowest rainfall, but tend to be sited in places close to services and where there is relative security from cattle raiding.

The future of forests and trees in Uganda will be much influenced by political, economic, and social factors. Uganda, as a political unit, came into existence between the late ninteenth century and 1926, achieving independence from Great Britain, the former protectorate power, in 1962. The 1980 national census gave a population of 12 630 075, equivalent to an average population density of 65 inhabitants per square kilometre of land-surface. In terms of mean monetary income per capita, the people are very poor. The country is classified by the United Nations as among the most impoverished. The only significant export is coffee, reliance on which has increased as copper, cotton, and tourism have declined. A large proportion of the country's foreign exchange is used for the purchase of transport-related items, including petroleum. There has been high monetary inflation during the past few years and, since salaries have not risen in line with the cost of living, many civil servants, including those in the Forest Department, suffer financial hardship. As an example, a young graduate in the Civil Service in 1982 might earn about 3000 shillings per month, a pittance when it is considered that a pair of good shoes costs about 15 000 shillings and his monthly fuel bill for domestic purposes, if he uses charcoal and lives in Kampala, could easily amount to 2000 shillings.

Two facts which have helped to soften the impact of these extremely harsh economic circumstances are that today, though probably not for much longer, nearly everybody in Uganda owns some land, and that many salary and wage earners on the government payroll have other sources of income to supplement their official earnings. Common part-time activities for foresters seem to include small-scale farming and dealing in commodities. One consequence is that many government servants find it difficult, both in terms of time and psychologically, to commit themselves wholly to their jobs. Another factor is that a substantial number of forestry officials, in common with members of many other institutions in Uganda, tend to treat the organization in which they are employed as existing partly for their personal benefit. It is easy to make illicit money in the Forest Department, with its control over one of the most valuable resources remaining in the country. All of this sometimes evokes a feeling of sadness in the older generation of civil servants, who remember with nostalgia the higher standards of earlier times in the Civil Service.

There are undoubtedly many political and social problems in Uganda, but the way in which one regards these problems is much influenced by ideology. However, most people would agree with Richards (1969) that the area of Africa now known as Uganda was culturally very diverse prior to the establishment of regular and direct contact with the outside world during the last century. There was a great diversity of political and economic systems, and the people spoke more than thirty languages belonging to no fewer than four major language groups. Various institutions and new ideas were introduced into Uganda during the period of British rule, and it was widely hoped that some of these would form the basis for national unity after independence. However, some of the new institutions have proved fragile, and there are also the complications of new social divisions based on imported religious faiths as well as a variety of political ideologies along the left-right spectrum. The country today is culturally very complex.

The role of forestry in relation to the social and political environment needs a lot of thought by the parties concerned. The Forest Department is one of those institutions introduced by the British, and forestry, as prac-tised by the Department, is an applied science, representing a body of ideas and techniques quite different from anything which existed in Uganda prior to its contact with Western influence. Few would disagree with the statement that a bright economic future is impossible unless organizations dealing with the environment, like the Forest Department, are informed and effective. Unfortunately, recent social and political developments have tended to reduce the capabilities of the Department, and much support is needed from both within and without the country to help reverse this downward trend.

Chapter 3

Environmental trends

There is a paucity of data on many aspects of national life—industry, agriculture, energy, transport, labour, household, culture, etc. For any data series (where there is data) there are gaps, inconsistencies and inaccuracies. This is particularly so for the decade of the 70s, during which there were no important data-collection operations mounted at national level. The last *Statistical Abstract* came out in 1972 and it essentially related to the late 60s. There was general stagnation or destruction of developmental projects and programmes in Uganda during the decade of the 70s and this adversely affected the national data infrastructure. (Kiregyera 1981, p. 601)

The information gap of the last ten to fifteen years is a serious constraint in planning for development in Uganda, particularly since it is thought that there have been major environmental and social changes during this period. To assess recent environmental developments, the author asked 35 students of Makerere University, 31 of whom were enrolled for a final-year course in plant ecology, to take home questionnaires during the 1981 Christmas vacation. When assessing environmental developments they were advised to consult their parents or other older people. It was fortunate that the students were well distributed throughout the country (Figure 1). The number of people taking part in this survey could have been increased, but I felt that there was an advantage in relying on a relatively small group of comparatively well motivated and informed people. On receipt of the completed questionnaires I was satisfied that at least 85% of the students had taken the exercise seriously. Even so, for any one question there were generally a few cases where the answer was omitted or muddled, and this is the reason why the figure for the total number of students given later is often less than 35.

Students were asked to comment on environmental changes which had occurred within 3-kilometre radii of their homes during the preceding 15 years (1966-1981). Wherever possible, the results are compared here with information available from other sources. It must be emphasized that, while I have considerable confidence in the trends reported by the students, I have more doubts about the actual figures which they provide. For example, while it will be obvious in most places whether or not there has been an appreciable growth in the population, assessments of percentage increases must be treated with caution in the absence of actual counts.

The first question concerned population change. Thirty-three students reported an increase and two a decrease, the declines being said to be special cases related to the effects and after-effects of the 'Liberation War' of 1978—9. The mean population increase over the 15-year period was 33.7% (average of 30 replies), giving an annual growth rate of 1.95%. Nearly everybody mentioned that there had been expansion of the established population, and 20 people stated that there had also been immigration from other areas. A major movement was said to be from Kigezi to Toro and Bunyoro.

Official population figures for the 1921—1980 period, based on chiefs' returns and national censuses, are given in Table 2. The mean estimate for the annual percentage population increase for 1966—1981 worked out from the students' figures (1.95%) is somewhat lower than the annual growth rates for 1959—1969 and 1969—1980 calculated from the census data (3.9% and 2.6% respectively). The high growth rate between 1959 and 1969 seen in the official figures is due partly to the arrival of a large number of people, mainly refugees, from other countries. The 1980 census, held at a time of political tension, cannot have been particularly accurate. According to the *National Report* of 1972, it is probable that there has been a steady rise in the annual growth rate of the established population (i.e. disregarding changes due to immigration and emigration) during the past 50 years, and the rate was estimated at 3.2% in 1969 and was projected to reach 3.5% by 1976. The 1980 census may therefore have considerably underestimated the size of the population.

The extent of internal migration over the last fifteen years is unknown, but must be substantial. Even before 1966 the Government was involved in resettlement schemes aimed at relieving land pressure, and there was also much unplanned population movement. According to the *Atlas of Uganda* of 1962, the main areas of land shortage in about 1960 were southern Teso, Bugisu, the lower slopes of Rwenzori, the plateau area of West Nile, and part of the districts of Busoga, Bukedi, and Kigezi. According to Mr J. B. Kibera of the Geography Department, Makerere University, important recent movement have been from Kigezi to Bunyoro, Toro, Mubende and Ankole, from Bugisu and Bukedi to Bunyoro, Busoga and elsewhere, and from West Nile to Bunyoro (personal communication). An interesting finding of the 1980 census was that some urban centres, including Jinja and Entebbe, have actually declined in population since 1969. The 1980 census

Table 2. Population growth in Uganda

Date	Population	Annual growth rate (%)
1921	2960000	1.8
1931	3554000	1.9
1949	4960000	2.6
1959	6536531	3.9
1969	9548847	2.6
1980	12630075	

Figures from National Report (Government of Uganda 1972) and Kabera (personal communication)

probably under-recorded the sizes of some urban populations, but even so it is true that there has not been the spectacular growth in the urban population characteristic of many African countries. This is doubtless partly because opportunities for urban employment in Uganda have been relatively few following the rundown or total collapse or many industries during the 1970s, and partly because of the very high cost of living in the monetary sector of the economy.

Climate was the subject of the next section of the questionnaire. Out of 31 respondents, 27 thought that there had been a trend towards decreased rainfall since 1966, three reported no change, and one considered that it had become wetter. Twenty-eight people regarded rainfall as having become less predictable, the remaining three recording no change (31 respondents). Most of the students thought that day temperatures had become higher, a number adding that it had also become colder at night. Several mentioned an increase in the amount of wind. In view of these replies it is not surprising that 29 students commented that climatic developments have made the work of the cultivator more difficult.

Assessment of the students' opinions about climate is difficult because such meteorological data as are available for the period under consideration have not been analysed and many are of doubtful reliability. Further consideration of possible climatic changes during recent years and also of the predicted effects of forest clearance and tree clearance on climate is given in Chapter 5.

In 27 out of 32 cases the area of land under cultivation is reported to have increased; the other five people recorded declines. The mean percentage change for the area of cultivated land over the 15-year period is an increase of 33.8% (average for 30 respondents).

Although I have been unable to find other estimates of exactly the same statistic for comparison, an increase in the area of cultivated land might be expected in view of the population growth and because there has been a trend towards lower crop yields per unit area of land (see later). On the other hand, a counterbalancing factor has been a big reduction in the acreage of coffee and cotton. Also, there is a physical limit to agricultural expansion in some regions. It has already been mentioned that even in 1958 substantial parts of Uganda were believed to have a land problem, in the sense that the fallow phase of the agricultural cycle had become too short. According to one estimate (USAID 1982), the population today is near its 'theoretical maximum' in many parts of Uganda. The meaning of this phrase is not very clear, but the fact that it is used at all does give some idea of the seriousness with which the land issue is perceived by some agricultural experts. USAID regards the populations of Busoga and Bukedi as standing at 94% of their theoretical maxima, those of East and West Mengo as being at 82% of capacity, and those of Masaka, Ankole, and Teso as being at 68% of capacity.

The students were asked to give, in order, the three most extensively grown crops in 1966 and 1981, and their replies show that remarkably large changes seem to have occurred. One way of analysing the results is in terms of changes in rank order. To clarify: if the three leading crops had been given in 1966 as (1) cotton, (2) maize, and (3) groundnuts, and in 1981 as (1) maize, (2) cassava, and (3) groundnuts, then cotton would have shown a decrease in its rank position, maize and cassava would have shown increases, and groundnuts would not have changed. Considering here only those crops mentioned by 10 or more students, changes in rank order are shown in Table 3, from which it can be seen that cassava, potatoes (mainly sweet potatoes), beans, and maize have all increased greatly and that the 'cash' crops, coffee and cotton, have registered dramatic falls. Reasons for the various trends were only occasionally supplied by the students, but several did note that financial returns were often higher with 'food' than 'cash' crops.

The declines in coffee and cotton production are well known and are a major cause of the current foreign-exchange crisis. Cotton production decreased from an annual average of 427 000 bales for the 1968—1973 period to an annual average of 115 000 bales during 1974—1980, and then to only 15 000 bales in 1980 (Bibangambah 1981). Coffee, the only major agricultural export today, has shown a shallower but still very steep decline, from 250 000 tons in 1969 to 103 000 tons in 1974 (ibid.). Over recent years about 30% of the coffee crop is said to have been smuggled across the borders (ibid.); this is perhaps not surprising since the purchase of coffee is a state monopoly in Uganda and recently the farmer has been

Table 3. Changes in rank order of crops

Crop	Increase in rank position	Same rank position	Decrease in rank position
Cassava	11	2	2
Potatoes (mainly sweet)	11	1	2
Beans	9	2	2
Maize	8	2	3
Bananas (including *Matoke*)	5	3	6
Millet	3	3	6
Groundnuts	3	2	7
Cotton	1	2	8
Coffee	2	1	10

Based on the three most widely-grown crops in each area in 1966 and 1981. Only crops mentioned by ten or more students are included.

receiving for his coffee only 15—20% of the price which he would expect to receive in an open-market economy (Begumis 1981). Regarding food crops, USAID (1982) also reports that there have been major changes in the proportions of different types of crops. In West Buganda, for example, *matoke* (cooking bananas) is said to have increased greatly, displacing other crops, and in the north, millet, sorghum, and groundnuts have declined in relative importance as cassava and sweet potatoes have increased.

Twenty-eight students reported a decline in crop yields per unit area of land; only four reported an increase (32 respondents). The main reason for declining yields was given as reduction in soil fertility, and this in turn was attributed by nearly all students to an insufficiently long resting period for the land.

I have been unable to find reliable figures of crop yields for recent years, but the trend observed by the students is widely mentioned by other people and is to be expected. The *National Report* states:

There is evidence to suggest that the yield of banana plantations is much lower now than in the past. Old men in banana-growing parts of Uganda claim that the bunches of bananas harvested now are much smaller than was the case thirty or so years ago. A casual survey of peasant plantations reveals that not only are the bunches smaller but also there are fewer fruiting stems per plantation.

Questions on weeds revealed no changes of importance. The most serious weeds in both 1966 and 1981 were *Bidens pilosa, Commelina* spp.,

Digitaria scalarum, Galinsoga parviflora, and *Oxalis latifolia*. This list is in remarkable agreement with one in the *National Report* in which all the above types are listed as being among the most important from the point of view of abundance and persistence. The other species mentioned in the *National Report* are *Acacia hockii, Cymbopogon afronardus, Imperata cylindrica*, and *Lantana camara*, all tough perennials of a different class from the point of view of the farmer and therefore not mentioned by the students.

Cattle were the most abundant livestock in most areas in both 1966 and 1981 (24 out of 35 cases in both years). Changes in the numbers of cattle, sheep and goats are shown in Table 4. A substantial increase in the pig population was noted by some students. Several reasons for changes in livestock numbers were given. The two which stand out are a decrease in the area of grazing land and a decline in the quality of the pasture. A decrease in the area available for grazing was noted in 27 out of 35 cases, and a decline in pasture quality in 30 out of 35 cases. The most commonly cited reason for the decline in pasture quality was overgrazing; climatic deterioration was also mentioned.

Table 4. Changes in numbers of domestic animals, 1966–1981

	Increase	No change	Decrease
Cattle	18	3	3
Sheep	3	10	21
Goats	7	8	19

Total number of respondents = 34

Considering now the vegetation, a decrease in the number of trees was widely reported, both as forest and as more scattered individual specimens in cultivated or savanna areas. Unfortunately, the term 'forest' was misunderstood by a few students, but nevertheless the general trend towards deforestation is clear from replies to a question on changes in the extent of forest: 26 people mentioned that the area of forest had declined, in 7 instances with complete forest elimination. It is noteworthy that nobody recorded either an increase in the area of forest or no change. Twelve people commented that there had been illegal encroachment into forest reserves. The number of trees outside forests was reported by 29 students to have declined, and only one person claimed no change; nobody reported an increase in the number of such trees. Of the 15 respondents who recorded a fall in the number of trees outside forests and who ventured a figure for the percentage change in numbers, the average works out as a fall of 50.5%, a startlingly high decline. The most frequently mentioned causes of forest and tree destruction were fuel collection and clearance for cultivation. An increase in the private planting of *Eucalyptus* was mentioned by some respondents, but in view of the recent difficulty of obtaining seedlings, much of this planting may well have been during the earlier rather than the later part of the period under consideration.

The extent of bush/scrub was said by 27 respondents to have decreased, and by 8 to have increased (35 replies). To deal first with the decreases, the most commonly mentioned causes were clearance for agriculture (cited by 25 out of 27 people), and fuel gathering. There is regional variation in the reasons given for bush/scrub increase: in the north, the increase was said to have been a consequence of overgrazing, while in the south it was attributed most commonly to the expansion of bush/scrub over land after forest had been destroyed.

There are regional differences too in the way that the amount of grassland has changed, with a tendency for increase in the north and west and decrease in the south and south-east (Table 5). Two major processes were said to be operating here, each with a different effect on grassland area. One is the clearance of woody vegetation, which can provide more grassland, and the other is the expansion of cultivation, with the opposite effect. The average height of grass was reported to have decreased in 28 cases, remained the same in one instance, and increased in 3 cases (32 respondents). The most common reason given for the shorter grass was overgrazing. Asked to assess changes in the abundance of particular grass species, respondents, as can be seen from Table 6, reported that less palatable types had increased at the expense of more valuable species.

Table 5. Changes in the extent of grassland, 1966—1981

Region	Increase	Decrease	Number of respondents	Respondent numbers
North	7	3	10	1—10
South and south-east	3	12	15	11—25
West and south-west	6	3	9	26—34
Totals	16	18	34	

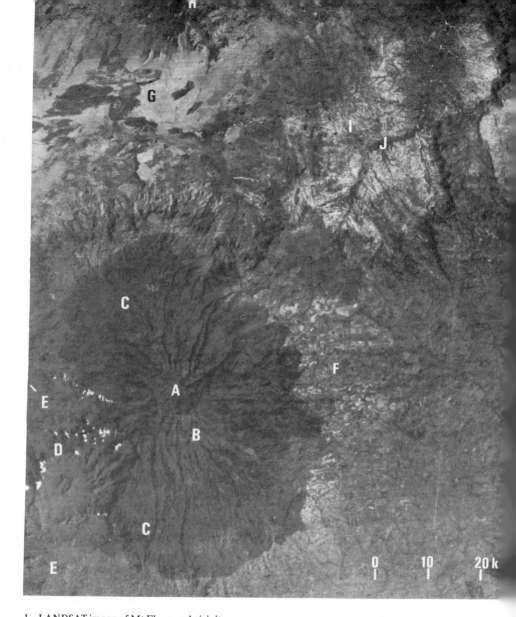

1. LANDSAT image of Mt Elgon and vicinity

   A. The Elgon caldera
   B. High altitude (ericaceous and afroalpine) vegetation
   C. Montane forest
   D. Nkokonjeru ridge, with clouds
   E. Intensive small-holding agriculture
   F. Large European-type farms in Kenya
   G. Burning scars in *Acacia* savanna
   H. Mt Kadam
   I. Heavily overgrazed land incapable of being burnt
   J. Denser vegetation near the River Suam and its tributaries

   Taken on 1 February 1973. (Plates 1—5 reproduced by kind permission of the Regional Remote Sensing Facility, Nairobi)

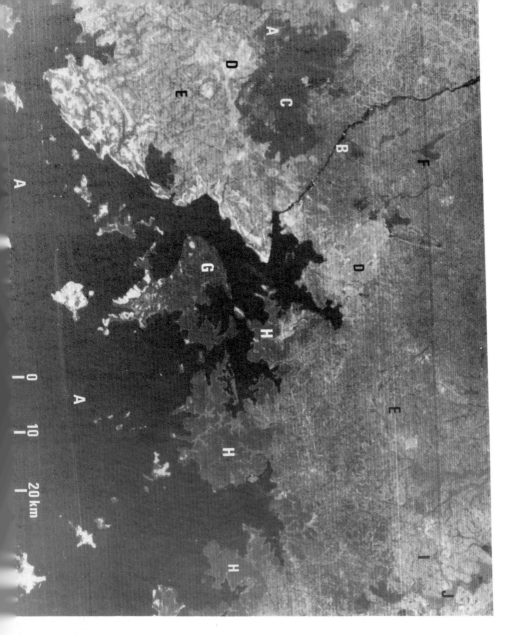

2. LANDSAT image of eastern Buganda and southern Busoga

A. Lake Victoria	F. Ngereka Forest
B. River Nile	G. Buvuma Island with much secondary forest
C. Mabira Forest	H. Secondary forest
D. Sugar estates	I. *Combretum* savanna
E. Largely small-holding agriculture	J. Swamp

Taken on 27 March 1976.

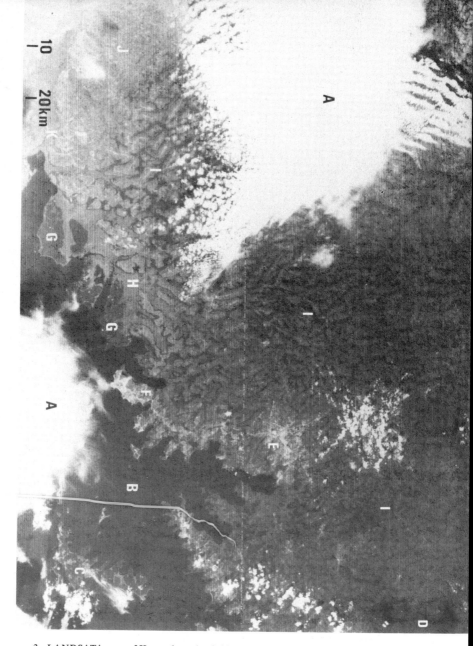

3. LANDSAT image of Kampala and neighbourhood
   A. Cloud
   B. Lake Victoria
   C. Kome Island with extensive forest
   D. Mabira Forest
   E. Kampala
   F. Entebbe
   G. Islands, largely secondary forest
   H. Permanent swamp
   I. Dendritic pattern of largely cultivated or grassy interfluves; forest on lower slopes; papyrus in valleys
   J. *Acacia* savanna
   K. The swamp-filled Katonga Channel

   Taken on 29 January 1974.

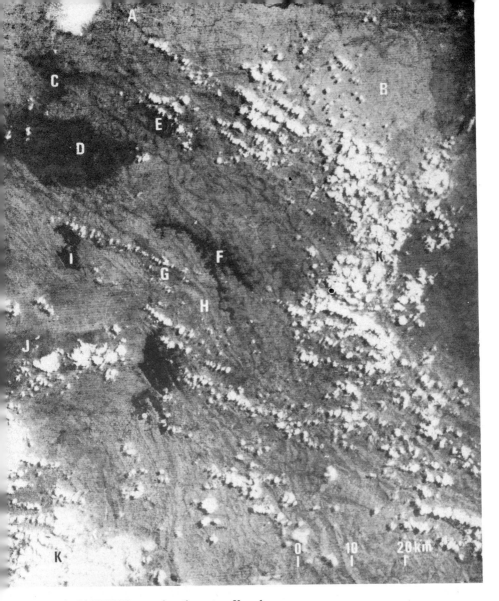

4. LANDSAT image of south-western Uganda

A. River Birira
B. Grass savanna
C. Kayonza Forest
D. Bwindi Forest
E. Mafuga Forest (a softwood plantation)
F. Lake Bunyonyi
G. Echuya Forest (a bamboo forest)
H. North-west/south-east folded rocks of the Karagwe-Ankolean System. This area is intensively cultivated.
I. Lake Mutanda
J. Bufumbira Volcanoes with summits under cloud
K. Cloud

Taken on 13 September 1972.

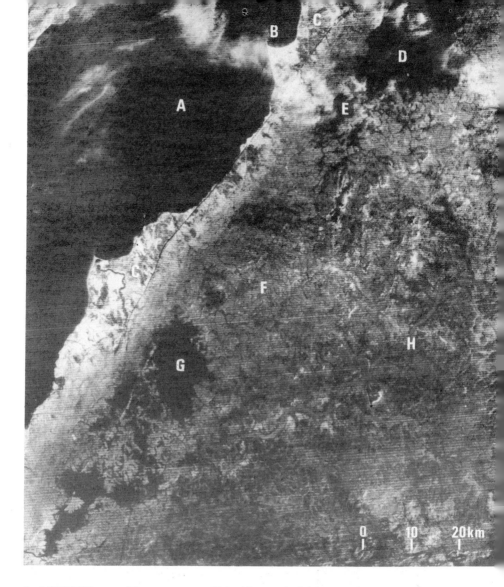

5. LANDSAT image of the eastern part of Lake Albert and adjoining country
   A. Lake Albert with streaks of cloud
   B. Butiaba
   C. Dry rift-valley flats near the lake with prominent burning scars and a low cover of vegetation
   D. Budongo Forest
   E. Siba Forest
   F. Agricultural land with forest patches, mainly along water courses
   G. Bugoma Forest
   H. Kafo Channel filled with swamp vegetation
   Taken on 24 December 1975.

6. The basal part of the canopy tree *Newtonia buchananii*, showing buttresses. This is a common tree in Uganda, but this photograph was taken in a forest patch on the southern side of Mt Meru, Tanzania.

Photographed December 1978 by the author.

7. The large canopy tree *Ficus mucosa* growing in seasonal swamp forest in Mpanga Forest near Kampala. This forest falls within the *Celtis-Chrysophyllum* Lowland Forest Zone.

Photographed about 1970 by the author.

8. A view of the canopy of swamp-edge forest near Entebbe. Taken from a tower. The central tree is *Musanga cecropioides*, which grows both in young secondary forest and in the Lake Victoria swamp forests. Behind is the palm *Raphia farinifera*. This forest lies within the *Piptadeniastrum* Lowland Forest Zone.

Taken in February 1982 by the author.

9. Bwindi Forest, Kabale District (Kigezi). Taken at an altitude of about 2300 m. This forest falls into the Moist Lower Montane Forest Zone.

Photographed in about 1967 by the author.

10. Clearing forest for farmland in Kabale District. Note the terracing. Photographed about 1967 by the author.

11. Mechanical logging in Budongo Forest. The main forestry interest here has been in various species of mahogany. Photographed in July 1967 by Sidney Hamilton.

12. A scene of devastation in Budongo Forest following mechanical logging. About 40 per cent of the topsoil is disturbed during this type of operation. At the time when this picture was taken the extraction of desirable species was followed by the widespread poisoning of weed trees.

Photographed in July 1967 by Sidney Hamilton.

13. *Loudetia* grassland near Entebbe, with forest thickets. The prominent tree is *Maesopsis eminii*, a favourite with foresters. This area would once have carried forest of the *Piptadeniastrum* Zone type, even though the soil is sandy and has frequent outcrops of laterite. Forest spread onto the grassland is today very slow, perhaps partly because of soil degradation following forest clearance.

Photographed about 1967 by the author.

14. The intensively farmed slopes of the western side of Mt Elgon taken from the forest-reserve boundary. The Nkokonjeru ridge may be seen in the background. This area would once have carried forest; today the main tree planted among the crops is *Eucalyptus*. The Mt Elgon forest reserve in this area has recently experienced widespread illegal encroachment.

Photographed about 1969 by the author.

15. Kabale District (Kigezi) showing agricultural land and the Bufumbira Volcanoes beyond. The hills in the foreground once carried moist lower montane forest; today the main tree species grown is *Eucalyptus*. Soil erosion has locally exposed bedrock. Note the line of the forest-reserve boundary on the volcanoes.

Photographed in April 1982 by the author.

16. The Lake Bunyonyi area of Kabale District (Kigezi). The plantation in the mid-distance was started as a local-government plantation of pine and cypress, but is now administered by the central Government. This scene would have been forest covered before the arrival of agriculture.

Photographed about 1967 by the author.

17. Tree stumps remaining in newly opened agricultural land near Rugege Forest in Rwanda. A planted boundary strip of exotic species helps to demarcate the boundary of the government forest on the left. Remains of terraces may be seen in the background, but no measures have been taken to alleviate soil erosion in the new enterprise.

Photographed in 1976 by Alan Perrott.

18. Private nursery at Kampala, growing *Eucalyptus* and cypress seedlings for sale.

Photographed in 1982 by the author.

19. Taro and maize growing on a reclaimed papyrus swamp near Kampala. Reclamation of such swamps was unknown until recently, but now is a major environmental development. Photographed in 1982 by the author.

Table 6. Changes in the abundance of named grasses, 1966—1981

Species	Increase	No change	Decrease	Total	Grazing value
Sporobolus spp.	21	2	7	30	Poor—nil
Cymbopogon afronardus	17	3	8	28	Nil
Imperata cylindrica	11	6	17	34	Poor
Hyparrhenia spp.	9	4	19	32	High—poor
Themeda triandra	6	6	16	28	Medium
Pennisetum purpureum	2	5	26	33	High

The classification in the last column follows Senyimba (unpublished).

There is very little published information to compare with the above results on vegetation change. John Aluma, Professor of Forestry at Makerere University, confirms that there has recently been a big reduction in the number of trees in many parts of the country. He describes parts of Acholi, Lango, and Teso as being miserably short of trees, and many other people have mentioned the same decline. Mr X. K. Ovon of the National Research Council reports that virtually all natural savanna trees in the south-west part of West Nile have been destroyed. Other informants have commented that tall grass is becoming scarce in some places. In Lango, tall grass, which is used for thatching, has become an item of commerce, which would have been unthinkable only ten years ago.

All 35 students answered a question on the types of water supply available. Wells and surface water were the main sources in both 1966 and 1981, with boreholes ranking third. An increase in piped supply over the period refers almost entirely to the southern Buganda/Jinja region. Regarding the quantity of water available over the year as a whole, there is reported to have been a decline in 23 cases, no change in 11, and an increase in one instance (35 respondents). Greater seasonal variation in water supply was noted in 19 cases, no change in 11, and less seasonality in 5 cases (35 replies). The single case of increased quantity and 2 of the 5 instances of decreased seasonal variation were due to the provision of a piped supply, and in general there appears to have been a marked deterioration in the availability of water over the 15-year period. The reason mentioned most often for this deterioration was increased climatic aridity, and only 5 people gave vegetational change in catchments as a possible cause. Water quality was said to have declined in 18 cases, shown no change in 9 cases, and improved in 5 cases (32 respondents). The latter were all related to the provision of a piped supply.

Decline in the extent of swamp was noted by 25 people, no change by 4, and an increase by one (30 replies). The two main causes of decline were given as increased climatic aridity and clearance for cultivation. The figures given in Table 7 suggest that the spread of swamp cultivation is a major new environmental development and this is confirmed by other informants as well as by my own observations. Another cause of swamp clearance mentioned by a few students is brick-making. This is a small-scale industry which has expanded tremendously over the last fifteen years, partly, it is said, to compensate for a shortage of wood for building. Bricks are often made from swamp clay and are sometimes fired, which is another cause of tree destruction.

Table 7. Were swamps cultivated?

	1966	1981
Yes	2	26
No	29	5

Number of respondents = 31

The main fuel in nearly all areas in both 1966 and 1981 was given as wood or, less frequently, its derivative, charcoal. Asked whether it had become easier or more difficult to obtain wood, 30 people recorded greater difficulty, 4 no change, and one greater ease. Not surprisingly, an increase in the distance needed to travel to obtain wood was noted in nearly all cases. Thirty-two people hazarded guesses about the average distance travelled to gather wood in 1966 and 1981, and these not only give an idea of the magnitude of the fuel problem but also highlight regional differences (Table 8). On average, people needed to travel about four times as far in 1981 as in 1966. The biggest percentage rise as well as the greatest absolute distances were in the north.

According to other sources of information, the use of charcoal in Uganda has increased very greatly over the last 10 years; it is employed almost entirely by richer urban dwellers. Charcoal is expensive and a family using charcoal in Kampala can expect to pay over 2,000 shillings per month for fuel. Electricity is much cheaper, though only available in a few localities, but it is very difficult to obtain electrical gadgets and their spare parts. For this reason the halls of residence at Makerere University have all switched over to charcoal, of which they consume vast quantities, even though all

Table 8. Mean distances from home travelled to obtain firewood

District	1966 (km)	1981 (km)	Percent increase	No. of respondents	Respondent code nos. (Fig. 1)
North	0.93	4.38	471	10	1—10
South and south-east	0.48	1.57	327	14	11—25
West	0.53	2.18	411	8	26—35
Total/mean	0.60	2.70	423	32	

possess modern electric kitchens. Among other energy sources of local importance are the dried stems and roots of non-woody plants. For example, the stems of *Conyza floribunda,* maize and sorghum, and the rhizomes of *Digitaria scalarum* are all used for this purpose in southern Kigezi, where they probably constitute the major source of fuel in parts of this tree-deficient district.

An increase in soil erosion was noted by 28 people, 5 thought that there had been no change, and 2 reported a decrease (35 replies). The majority regarded sheet wash as the most prevalent type of erosion. Further evidence of soil deterioration is that the extent of bare ground was said to have increased in 25 out of 33 cases, the texture of the topsoil to have become sandier in 17 out of 30 cases (with 11 reports of no change), and the colour of the topsoil to have become lighter in 26 out of 31 cases. Many students mentioned a decrease in soil fertility; no one thought that the soil had become more fertile.

The abundance of large wild animals was said by 29 out of 30 students to have declined. Many people mentioned that there were no, or virtually no, larger wild animals remaining in their areas. Hunting is no longer a major activity (Table 9).

Table 9. Was hunting an important activity?

	1966	1981
Yes	15	1
Occasional activity	16	12
No	1	19
Total number of replies	32	32

Finally, the students were asked about the availability of assistance from government agricultural and veterinary departments; the results suggest deterioration of both services (Table 10). Reasons given for the declines were decreased professionalism, transport problems, low availability of agrochemicals and other commodities, and the general economic decline.

Table 10. Was advice and assistance more readily available in 1966 or 1981?

	From Department of Agriculture	From Veterinary Department
More in 1966	22	22
Same	5	4
More in 1981	5	7
Total No. of respondents	32	33

To summarize this survey, the following environmental trends were reported to have occurred between the years 1966 and 1981:

—the population increased;
—the climate became more arid;
—the area of cultivated land increased;
—the 'export' crops, cotton and coffee, declined;
—crop yields per unit area declined, probably mainly because of reduced soil fertility;
—the quantity and quality of grass fodder declined;
—the number of trees decreased;
—non-piped water supplies became dirtier and less reliable;
—the area of swamp declined and there was an increase in swampland cultivation;
—fuel became scarcer;
—large wild animals became rare;
—government agricultural and veterinary services declined in quality.

Recognition of these trends does not minimize the importance of local exceptions to the general pattern, but in general the results of this survey indicate considerable environmental deterioration. This will inevitably have very serious economic and social consequences if allowed to continue unchecked.

Chapter 4

The forests

There are reasons to suppose that a considerable proportion of the forest shown on the vegetation map of Uganda drawn in the later 1950s (Figure 2) has now been destroyed. To gain a more up-to-date picture of the distribution of forest I visited the Regional Remote Sensing Facility in Nairobi, an institution which receives from the United States imagery of eastern Africa collected by the LANDSAT satellites. Each LANDSAT satellite, of which there have sometimes been two in diametrically opposite orbits, passes over Uganda every eighteen days and, since this has been happening for about a decade, it might be supposed that an immense quantity of data has been collected on changes in the distribution of some natural resources, including forest. However, due to the frequent occurrence of cloud and other problems, there are no photographs at all of some forested areas and elsewhere it is often impossible to compare the forest cover of different years. An attempt has nevertheless been made to put together a map of the distribution of forest based on LANDSAT imagery (Figure 3). A serious limitation of this map is that none of the pictures used is very recent and it is shown from other sources that some forests have recently been diminishing rapidly in size. Also, the images vary in the dates on which they were taken, between 13 September 1972 and 7 March 1979 (the dates are shown on the figure). In those cases where there is a choice, I have used the clearest pictures for the purpose of map construction. The baseline map used for Figure 3 is the 1:1,000,000 map compiled by the Department of Lands and Surveys in 1962—3, which is shown by the satellite photographs to be inaccurate in places, particularly towards the south-east.

The photographs on which the new forest map is based were printed in 'standard false colour', which refers to the selection by the photographic technician of a particular combination of wavebands and filters that has been found satisfactory for a wide variety of applications. Dense, actively photosynthesizing vegetation appears red. Examination of the Ugandan photographs reveals that the ease with which forest is distinguishable from

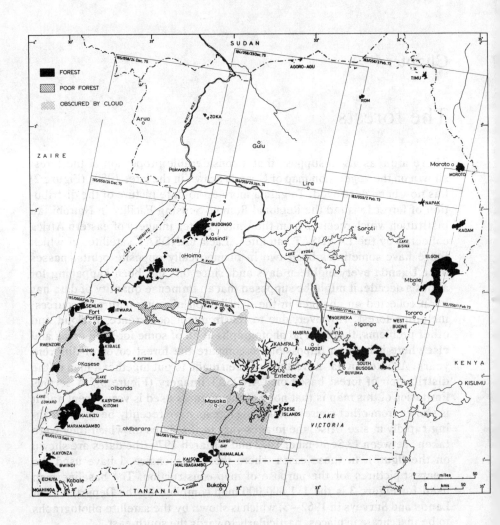

Figure 3. · Forest distribution in Uganda in the mid-1970s

Based on interpretation of LANDSAT imagery. The satellite tracks pass diagonally across Uganda from north to south.

other vegetation types varies from frame to frame, being more difficult when intermediate types of vegetation such as secondary forest and thicket are present, and also depending on the seasonal state of the vegetation. The following frame-by-frame interpretation is based mainly on published information about each area, assisted by my personal knowledge and also aided by an independent interpretation of the satellite imagery by Carvalho (1982). The numbers used for the frames are the standard LANDSAT codes (given on the figure).

185/058: West Nile and neighbourhood. The only natural forest identified is Zoka in East Madi, standing out clearly as two small, well separated blocks. The forest area is less than that shown on the 1950s vegetation map (Figure 2), on which Zoka is drawn as one block, not two. Perhaps the forest has shrunk and become fragmented. In addition to Zoka, there are a few other red spots on this frame, but these are believed not to be natural forest. Many of those in West Nile are plantations of exotic trees, while some of those towards the top and right of the photograph may be thickets of lowland bamboo (*Oxytenanthera abyssinica*).

185/059: Lake Albert area. Budongo, Bugoma, and Itwara Forests stand out clearly. Near Budongo and Bugoma there are a number of small out-liers of forest too small to include on the map. The forest blocks marked in Bwamba lie within a bright pink zone which, according to Malpas (personal communication), is swamp forest rich in oil palms (*Elaius guineensis*). This pink zone has not been mapped. The areas hatched on this and neigh-bouring frames are red in colour on the images, but not as intensely red as areas known to be mature forest, such as Budongo. The boundaries of these areas are poorly defined and difficult to map. Judging by the *Atlas of Uganda*, the vegetation of these areas is secondary forest and thicket. This is a part of Uganda which is thought to have once carried a much higher population than it did in the 1950s.

185/060: Lake George area. This is a poor-quality image with much cloud. Rwenzori Forest is almost totally obscured, Bwamba Forest cannot be clearly seen, and the boundary of Kibale Forest is difficult to trace, es-pecially in the north. A number of small burnt patches are present within Kibale Forest; these are probably in the grassland glades which are a feature of this forest. A forest, Kisangi, present to the north of Lake George in the 1950s (Figure 3), cannot be seen and is believed to have been cleared for agriculture (see Chapter 7). Kalinzu and adjoining Mara-magambo Forest are fairly distinct, as also is the western edge of Kasyoha-Kitomi. The eastern edge of the latter forest is, however, rather obscure;

the reason for this, according to the memoirs of the 1950s vegetation survey and also Rwaburindore (personal communication) is that the forest here is youthful and grades into other vegetation types. The extensive presence of colonizing forest in Kasyoha-Kitomi has been noted by Synnott (1971).

185/061: Kigezi. Kayonza-Bwindi Forest shows up very distinctly, but the outlines of Mgahinga and Echuya Forests cannot be clearly discerned, the former being obcured by cloud. The neck between Kayonza and Bwindi is narrower than on the vegetation map of the 1950s. Mafuga Forest, which is mainly a softwood plantation, is slightly lighter in colour than the natural forest of Bwindi-Kayonza.

184/058: Acholi. Some red dots towards the top of this frame, notably on Rom and in Agoro-Agu Forest Reserve, are probably patches of montane forest. Otherwise forest is absent.

184/059: West Kyoga area. There are some forests near the edges of this frame in the zones of overlap with adjoining frames; they are discussed under these frames. Otherwise forest is absent.

184/060: Buganda. Large areas are badly obscured by cloud, but Mabira and the forests on Busi and other islands surrounded by swamp to the west of Entebbe are clearly visible. Mabira Forest contains many clearings. Comparison with the vegetation map of the 1950s indicates that there has been some retreat of forest in the north-west and west. A feature of this frame is the extensive development of linear red areas, particularly to the west of Kampala. Some at least of these are known to be good forest and a not very successful attempt has been made to map them. The linear pattern is due mainly to the persistence of valley-bottom forest in a predominantly agricultural landscape, but unfortunately it is impossible to distinguish in parts of this frame between mature forest, degraded swamp forest, and herbaceous swamp vegetation, all known to be present.

184/061: Sango Bay. Forest is restricted to the hinterland of Sango Bay, but its exact extent is uncertain. Purple patches on the photograph are believed to be definitely forest and have been marked as such on the map, but the status of nearby less intensely purple areas is less certain. The latter, which have not been mapped, could possibly represent productive non-forest vegetation.

183/058: Karamoja. Forest is found only as localized patches on mountains and hills. There is a fairly extensive red area on Mt Moroto, and some of this, though not all, is believed to be forest. The forests in Timu and Nyangea-Napore Forest Reserves have imprecise outlines and are much smaller than on the vegetation map of the 1950s.

183/059: East Kyoga area. Forest is present extensively on Mt Elgon and locally on Mt Napak and Mt Kadam. The outline of the forest on Elgon is clear, with a distinct cut-line lower boundary, but, as with Mt Moroto, it is less certain how much of the red areas on Napak and Kadam represents forest. A red spot to the west of Mt Elgon, near Mbale, and of the same shade as the natural forest on Elgon, is known to be a *Eucalpytus* plantation. Several satellite images, taken between 10 December 1973 and 4 December 1980, are available for Elgon and a careful comparison of these by Carvalho (1982) has shown that the extent of forest has shrunk on the north, with retreat of the lower forest boundary.

183/060: Busoga. The outlines of Mabira, West Bugwe, and the forest to the west of West Bugwe show up distinctly. Forest is somewhat less extensive on Buvuma Island and on the mainland of southern Busoga than is indicated on the 1950s vegetation map. Extensive parts of these latter forests have a similar appearance to areas interpreted as secondary forest and thicket near Mubende (see comments for frame 185/059), suggesting that these too are immature. This is not surprising, since much of the forest here is known to have sprung up following depopulation during a sleeping-sickness epidemic at the beginning of the present century (*Uganda Journal* 1948; Langdale-Brown 1960).

182/059: Elgon area. The Elgon forests show up clearly on this image.

Certain points emerge from this study. First, forest is not a particularly common type of vegetation in Uganda and there is certainly no room for complacency regarding the conservation of the surviving remnants, for whatever purpose they are used. Second, the forests are generally widely separated from one another, forming ecological islands surrounded by a sea of other vegetation types. Third, Forest Department maps (e.g. Figure 5) show that nearly all forests are contained within forest reserves. Fourth, the distribution of forest during the 1970s was much the same as it was during the late 1950s, but there is evidence of forest retreat in several places and it is known that a major part of the recent forest destruction is not recorded on the satellite images, some of which are relatively old.

The forests do not represent a homogeneous resource and there is a lack of knowledge of their variability, which handicaps planning. However, there are fairly complete lists of tree species for some forests and it is also often known which are the commoner species. Several classifications of the forests have been proposed. Those followed here are that of Langdale-Brown *et al.* (1964) as modified by Hamilton (1974) for lowland forests and that of Hamilton (1982) for montane forests. Lowland and montane forests grade into one another (Hamilton 1975), and the altitudinal boundary between them is here arbitrarily taken as lying at about 1500 m.

Four types (or zones) of lowland forest may be recognized in Uganda, each being named after characteristic trees. All of these types are tall evergreen or semi-deciduous rain forests, typically with several storeys of trees and canopies over 30 m tall. These types are: (1) the *Parinari* Zone, which is virtually confined to western Uganda. It was also represented up to the 1960s in Namatale Forest on the lower slopes of Mt Elgon, but Namatale has probably now been cleared; (2) the *Celtis-Chrysophyllum* Zone, represented both in western Uganda and in the Lake Victoria region; (3) the *Cynometra-Celtis* Zone, which is confined to western Uganda; and (4) the *Piptadeniastrum* Zone, which is found only close to Lake Victoria, replacing the *Celtis-Chrysophyllum* Zone within about fifteen kilometres of the lake. In Western Uganda there is a close relationship between altitude and the distribution of the three lowland forest zones which occur there, and this is shown even within a single forest, such as Kibale. The *Parinari* Zone is found above 1400 m, the *Celtis-Chrysophyllum* Zone at 1000—1400 m, and the *Cynometra* Zone at about 700—1200 m. The intolerance of species to relatively cold temperatures is believed to be a significant factor in determining the distribution of these three forest types, limiting the degree to which species are able to extend their ranges to higher altitudes. A second major factor is thought to be the relatively high moisture requirements of some species; this is especially significant in determining the extent to which species are able to extend their altitudinal ranges to lower altitudes. In the Lake Victoria region, the *Piptadeniastrum* and *Celtis-Chrysophyllum* Zones occur at similar altitudes and grade into one another (Sangster 1950). Rainfall tends to be higher in the *Piptadeniastrum* Zone and the soils are often sandier and much richer in phosphate.

Four montane forest zones are found in Uganda, their distributions being related to the decline in temperature which occurs with increasing altitude and variations in climatic moistness. (1) The Upper Montane Forest Zone is present at about 3050—3300 m on all mountains of sufficient height and degree of soil maturity (Rwenzori, Elgon, Sabinio, Mgahinga). This is a low forest type (15 m) with few species. (2) The Bamboo (*Arundinaria alpina*) Zone is found at c. 2450—3050 m on climatically wet mountains (Rwenzori, Elgon, Sabinio, Mgahinga). Bamboo is dominant at exceptionally low altitudes (2260—2450 m) in Echuya Forest, where it probably represents a colonizing community on ground once cleared by man. Bamboo is absent from the dry Karamoja mountains. (3) The Moist Lower Montane Forest Zone occurs at 1500—2450 m in climatically moist places and is recorded from Bwindi Forest, Rwenzori, and the western and southern slopes of Mt Elgon. This forest type is structurally rather similar to lowland forest. (4) The Dry Lower Montane Forest Zone is present at 2000—3050 m in drier areas, principally north-east Elgon and the mountains of Karamoja. Evergreen sclerophyllous trees are abundant in this forest type.

Little is known about the ways in which forests function as living systems in Uganda, and this is a very serious drawback to good management. The best known ecological investigations are those of Eggeling working in Budongo Forest (Eggeling 1940, 1947, 1948a, 1948b). Eggeling believed that the four forest types that he recognized are related to one another in two overlapping successional series. According to this view, two colonizing types, *Maesopsis* forest on richer soils and woodland forest (with *Olea welwitschii*) on poorer soils, are both said to develop into mixed forest, which is rich in mahoganies and lacks single-species dominance. Mixed forest, in turn, is believed eventually to give way to *Cynometra* forest, with much *Cynometra alexandri*. The interpretation of mixed forest as an intermediate stage in forest development has proved economically significant in that it has helped to determine methods of forest management (see Chapter 6). However, Eggeling's ideas have not gone unchallenged. Laws *et al.* (1970), noting that *Cynometra* is less susceptible to damage by elephants than many other species, including the mahoganies, have argued that *Cynometra* forest is a climax induced by elephants. The regeneration of one of the mahoganies, *Entandrophragma utile,* has been studied in detail in Budongo Forest by Synnott (1975), who reported that although this species grows best in partial shade it can regenerate successfully even under a dense canopy. The implication is that mahogany-rich forest may not necessarily be an unstable vegetation type, as thought by Eggeling. Synnott (1971) has also commented on the status of forest types within the West Ankole forests of Maramagambo, Kalinzu, and Kasyoha-Kitomi. He suggests that mixed forest may be a climax type on better soils and that forests tending towards single-species dominance, either by *Cynometra* or *Parinari,* could be associated with poorer sites. A similar view regarding *Cynometra* forest has been expressed by Osmaston (1959) in respect of Bugoma Forest. Synnott's study of *Entandrophragma utile* is noteworthy for being the first and perhaps only in-depth published investigation of the ecology of a particular forest-tree species in Uganda.

In the course of its work the Forest Department has undertaken inventories of the density and size distribution of tree species in many of its forests. A surprising result is that some of the taller and commoner species apparently have unstable age/size relationships (Philip 1962), meaning that these species seem to have an insufficient number of young individuals to guarantee that their abundance will continue to be maintained. In Kalinzu Forest, for example, there is insufficient regeneration of *Parinari excelsa* for the continuation of the dominant cover of *Parinari*. One suggestion is that in some forests the common trees may undergo autogenous cycles in abundance (Eggeling 1948a); thus, in Kalinzu Forest, there could be an alternation between two forest types, one dominated by *Parinari* and the other by such species as *Strombosia scheffleri* and *Drypetes* sp., which at present are common as small individuals beneath the *Parinari* canopy. Also, climatic fluctuations and human influences are certainly other causes of instability in Ugandan forests. Regarding the latter, it has been stated that all well-drained forests in central Buganda, including Mabira Forest, are growing on land which has been cleared at one time or another for agriculture (Philip 1962).

The distribution of species of forest plants and animals in Uganda is determined not only by modern environmental conditions but also by historical factors (Hamilton 1974; Kingdon 1971; Struhsaker 1981). During the arid period of the last Ice Age (which ended about 12 000 years ago), certain places in tropical Africa remained climatically favourable for forest development, providing refugia for the survival of forest species. The nearest major refugium to Uganda was centred on the rising ground of eastern Zaire and extended into south-western Uganda. When the rainfall increased 12 000 years ago there was an expansion in the area climatically favourable for forest and some species of forest organisms were able to expand their ranges quickly. Other species, however, possessed dispersal mechanisms poorly adapted for rapid spread or were held back by competition from more successful plants and animals. The result is that today there is a gradient of declining numbers of forest species extending from the south-west of Uganda towards the north and east, a general feature found in all lowland forests and wetter types of montane forest. Two of the richer forests in terms of numbers of species are Bwindi-Kayonza and Bwamba, both lying on the fringes of, or relatively close to, the former eastern Zaire refuge area (Hamilton 1976, 1981a; Kingdon 1973; van Someren and van Someren 1949).

A notable achievement since the late 1960s has been the continued operation of a small ecological field centre in Kibale Forest. This station, supported by the New York Zoological Society, has been especially valuable for its long-term studies of primates (McKey *et al.* 1978; Oates 1974; Struhsaker 1975, 1981), but other research has not been neglected and some of this has implications for methods of managing the forests for timber production. Comparison between areas which have been heavily logged by commercial operators and areas which have remained un-harvested has shown that heavy felling very seriously suppresses tree regeneration (Kalina, personal communication). An inference could be that lighter and perhaps more frequent tree felling might give a higher sustain-able timber yield than the present method of harvesting, which approaches clear-felling. Poor regeneration in heavily harvested areas is partly a result of the suppression of young trees by the dense shrub and climber tangle which develops in such open places (see also Forest Department 1960) and partly a consequence of a massive increase in the rodent population. The rodents quickly kill off any seedlings which happen to appear.

Floras covering the forest trees of Uganda have been published by Eggeling and Dale (1951) and Hamilton (1981b), and the authoritative *Flora of Tropical East Africa* (1952 *et seq.*) is available for many families. Despite some taxonomic uncertainties, the total number of species of forest trees is thought to be only about 450, a low figure in comparison with some other areas of tropical forest, such as Malaysia. Lists of plant species for some forests in western Uganda have been compiled by Synnott (1971), and the timber characteristics of many of the commoner species are described by Tack (1969). An account of the mammals is contained in Kingdon (1971), and a list of forest insects is given in Brown (1967).

Not all forests in Uganda are composed of indigenous species. The commonest exotic conifers in plantations are *Pinus patula*, *P. radiata* and *Cupressus lusitanica*. Many small areas of Black Wattle, *Acacia mearnsii,* were established earlier this century in Kigezi. These wattle plantations have not been maintained. Today *Eucalyptus* is probably the most widely planted tree in Uganda. A number of species are grown, usually in small wood-lots or as single trees. This genus is likely to become the main source of many wood products over large parts of the country in the years to come (Karani 1972), and is likely to be favoured by the Forest Department as a component of many agroforestry schemes. Advantages of *Eucalyptus* are often rapid growth and straight form, and the wood is useful for many purposes, though difficult to saw into planks and liable to snap under pressure. However, *Eucalyptus* should not be regarded as a universal panacea. Widespread planting raises the risk of catastrophic loss through disease, a common problem with monocultures. Serious attention should be given to the deleterious effects which the oils produced by the genus are alleged to have on the soil. Degradation of the soil is also a potential hazard with conifers.

To conclude this chapter, it should be stressed that knowledge of Uganda's forests is still small. This is of serious concern, because management of the forests should be built on a foundation of well established knowledge.

Chapter 5

Trees, climate and water

Two of the most important truths about rainforest are that more research is
needed to establish the facts; and that it will be impossible to wait for the facts
before acting. (Caulfield 1982)

When the future of tree resources in Uganda was first seriously considered
(Nicholson 1929, 1930), it was argued that forest conservation and tree-
planting programmes would help to ensure climatic conditions favourable
to agriculture. Since then, this argument has been heard less frequently as
forest has increasingly been seen more as a competitor than an ally of
agriculture. However, if it is true that trees really do help to improve the
agricultural climate, then the current massive rate of reduction in the
number of trees is an even more serious matter than is at first apparent.

The detection of any possible influences of human activities on climate is
complicated by the existence of 'natural' climatic fluctuations, occurring on
several quite different temporal scales. On a time-scale of thousands to
tens of thousands of years, there are known to have been major alterations
in temperature and rainfall, associated for instance with the glacial/
interglacial sequence (Hamilton 1982), but variations of the order of a few
years or a few decades are of greater interest in the present context. Unfortunately, no detailed analyses of recent rainfall variations seem to have
been carried out, and there is a problem with the data; at best, measurements of rainfall go back only to about the beginning of the twentieth
century and, as pointed out in Chapter 3, some of the records are untrust-
worthy. However, underlying considerable year-to-year variation of very
uncertain origin there may be more regular fluctuations. There are correla-
tions between the well-known 11-year sunspot cycle and variations in
rainfall over extensive parts of Africa, including the Sahel (Faure 1982)
and Ethiopia (Street-Perrott 1982; Wood and Lovett 1974). Fluctuations
in the level of Lake Victoria showed a high correlation with this cycle
during the early years of the present century, though the correlation broke
down after 1930 (Wood and Lovett 1974). Another climatic cycle which may

occur in Uganda is the 31-year cycle which Faure (1982) has found in the Sahel. It is also possible, and certainly believed by many Ugandans, that the dry seasons have tended to become longer during recent years, a trend which could possibly be a consequence of tree destruction. A similar trend has been reported from Nigeria (Hopkins 1962). There is some urgency in undertaking further research into rainfall patterns in Uganda, since, if more were known, it might be possible to undertake advanced planning to ameliorate the effects of droughts and floods.

It is unfortunate that very few experiments to study the effects of changes of vegetation on climate and the movement of water have been carried out in East Africa. There is a particularly critical lack of experimental knowledge about the influence of tree clearance on rainfall (Golding 1970). It has been suggested that because 'natural' rainfall fluctuations are known to occur and because there is no experimental evidence from Uganda that forest clearance reduces rainfall, there is no need to be concerned about the climatic effects of tree destruction. The logic is spurious, but nevertheless the shortage of hard evidence does weaken the case of the forest conservationist. However, there is less doubt about the influence of forest clearance on some other aspects of the water cycle, such as runoff, infiltration, and stream flow. Theoretical considerations and much anecdotal evidence of these effects are supported by experimental studies carried out in a few East African catchments in the late 1950s and early 1960s by the East African Agricultural and Forestry Research Organisation (Pereira 1967a, 1967b). These studies, the results of which have been incorporated into the account in this chapter, involved comparisons of closely situated catchments before and after land-use change was initiated in one of each group. The two main subjects were the effect of replacing montane forest by tea estates near Kericho in Kenya and the effect of replacing bamboo forest by softwood plantations on the Aberdares, also in Kenya. There was a less complete investigation into the effects of controlling grazing pressure on degraded land in Karamoja.

Because of the shortage of experimental evidence, I here make a hypothetical comparison between the climate and water balance of a typical Ugandan catchment covered with undisturbed forest and the same area cleared of trees and supporting overgrazed grassland (Figure 4). While a change from forest to overgrazed grassland is a very common event, forest clearance often results in a reduction in the total number of trees (frequently with a change in the types of trees present), rather than in their complete elimination. In a similar vein, the starting point in drier regions of Uganda is commonly not forest but wooded savanna. In the absence of experimental studies it may be reasonably assumed that the influences on climate and water conservation of vegetation with an intermediate density of trees are intermediate between the extremes of forest and treeless grassland.

The energy budgets of the contrasting vegetation types are discussed first. Note that, for the sake of simplicity, the complicating effects of diurnal variation are not considered. The quantity of incoming short-wave radiation reaching the ground from the sun will probably be much the same with the two vegetation types, though relatively reduced with the forest due to a greater incidence of cloud and relatively reduced with the grassland due to a greater incidence of dust and smoke. The two vegetation types will, however, contrast significantly in reflectivity (albedo), the forest reflecting perhaps about 11—14% of the incoming short-wave radiation and the grassland between about 4 and 6% more (the albedo estimates are taken from Dickinson (1980) and Henderson-Sellers (1980); if much bare ground is exposed after forest clearance, as it is with many agricultural practices in Uganda, then the albedo is likely to be greatly increased). It is undisputed that the forest will absorb an appreciably greater amount of energy than the grassland.

Energy absorbed by vegetated surfaces is released in various forms, of which three are of significance for the purposes of the present discussion. These are latent heat energy used in evaporating water from the plants and the soil (evapotranspiration), sensible heat, which is eventually transferred to the air, and outgoing long-wave radiation. It is agreed that, related to the lower albedo of the forest, the sum of latent heat energy and sensible heat energy will be higher with forest than with grassland (Charney 1975a and b; Dickinson 1980; Henderson-Sellers 1980; Ripley 1976). The next consideration is that water loss through evapotranspiration will be much higher with forest (Barry and Chorley 1976; Oke 1978). This will certainly be the case during periods of dry weather and also on an annual basis, but it is argued by Dickinson (1980) that during rainy periods the loss of water can be higher from short grassland than from forest. If the grassland is burnt, as it usually is, this will serve to reduce water loss from the grassland to the atmosphere even further. However, remembering that the total amount of energy absorbed by the forest is greater than in the case of the grassland, there is some uncertainty about which of the two types of vegetation will display greater sensible heat transfer to the atmosphere in absolute terms. Probably the forest will be slightly cooler, especially during dry seasons (Henderson-Sellers 1980; McCulloch and Dagg 1962; Penman 1963; Ripley 1976). It follows that the amount of energy lost by long-wave radiation will probably be slightly less with forest than with grassland, since energy loss through radiation is largely a function of temperature (Penman 1963; see also Henderson-Sellers 1980).

If rainfall is now considered, the important question immediately arises whether or not this is increased by the presence of forest (FAO 1962). It

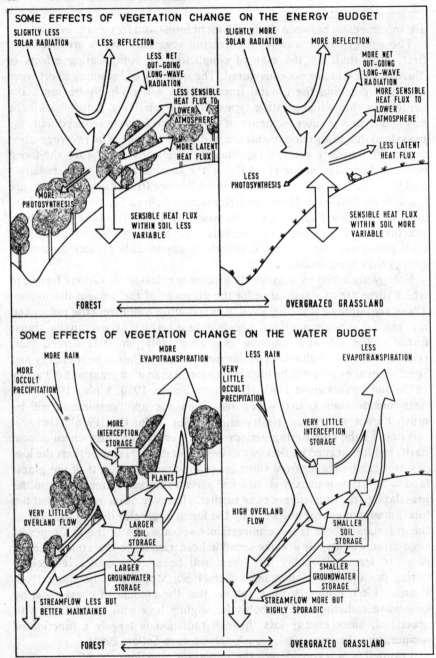

Figure 4. Energy and water budgets of forest and overgrazed grassland

may be noted that there is no doubt from the existence of the forest zone stretching up to 80 km inland from Lake Victoria that the nature of the local surface can greatly influence the regional climate in Uganda. Major considerations regarding the forest/rainfall relationship are that rainfall in Uganda is overwhelmingly convectional and local, and that even a slight upward movement of air can trigger the building of cumulus cloud and initiate rain (Boucher 1975). Two factors which make such triggering more likely with forest than with grassland are the greater surface roughness of the forest (Rutter 1975) and the greater instability of the air above it. The reason for the latter is that, regardless of whether sensible heat transfer is greater or less with forest than with grassland, the air overlying a forest will certainly be moister and the total (sensible + latent) energy imparted to the lower layers of the atmosphere from the forest will be greater. The reduction in total energy transfer to the lower atmosphere, which occurs when forest is cleared, is believed by Charney *et al.* (1976) to be the significant factor in decreasing the chances of convective precipitation. Overall, the current consensus seems to be that the presence of forest will increase rainfall (e.g. Charney 1975a and b; Charney *et al.* 1976; Golding 1970; McCulloch and Dagg 1962; Potter *et al.* 1975), but what remains in doubt is the scale of this effect (Farnworth and Golley 1974; Goudie 1981; Ripley 1976; Sagan *et al.* 1979). Little progress seems to have been made with such questions as the influence of forest size, the effect of varying tree density in a savanna or agricultural landscape, and the degree to which the climatic benefits of forest are carried beyond a forest boundary.

Water from the atmosphere is gained by plant/soil systems not only through the fall of rain and hail, but also through occult (hidden) precipitation, involving the interception of mist by vegetation and the subsequent drip or flow of some of the condensed water down to the ground. Although measurements are scarce, occult precipitation is believed to supply significant quantities of water in some world forests (Hewlett 1967). Judging by casual observations, occult precipitation is unlikely to be a major factor in Uganda except in some montane forests and perhaps also in some valleys in the lowlands. Occult precipitation is unlikely to be significance in overgrazed grassland.

Some of the rain falling on a vegetated surface fails to reach the ground, being intercepted by the aerial parts of plants and subsequently evaporated (Oke 1978). This 'interception storage' has a much larger capacity in forest than grassland. There has been some debate about the extent to which interception losses help to conserve water within the ecosystem (Zinke 1967), the argument being that the intercepted water might largely replace water which would otherwise have been lost by transpiration. However, according to Rutter (1975), much of the water intercepted by a forest is evaporated rather quickly, and it can be regarded as replacing water loss by transpiration only to a very limited extent. Interception storage deprives plants in forests of the immediate benefits of some of the rain falling on the vegetation, but it does contribute to the maintenance of a relatively humid climate, helping to give a high precipitation, and it is unlikely to represent a net loss to the forest water balance on a medium-term time-scale.

Forest soil are well known to be much more permeable to water than those of overgrazed grassland (Pierce 1967). This relatively high permeability of forest soils is due to their thicker litter horizons, the greater quantity of organic matter in their topsoils, greater activity by soil organisms, and a decreased tendency for soil pores to become blocked by finer soil particles, as well as other factors. It is a readily observable fact that the movement of water along the surface of the ground inside a forest during a storm is minimal and that such water as can be seen on the surface is clear. In contrast, overgrazed grassland is notorious for its high overland flow of water, often brightly coloured by a high content of suspended soil particles. Given the greater transpiration and decreased overland flow of forest, it is perhaps not surprising that less water is available on an annual basis in streams supplied by a forested catchment than is the case with grassland (Hibbert 1967). However, the overwhelming advantages of maintaining a forest cover in a catchment are that the water is much cleaner and that the flow of water is more evenly maintained throughout the year, reducing the risks of catastrophic floods and low flows or even no flows at all. The clearance of vegetation in catchment areas is recognized as one of the world's major environmental problems, involving the degradation of hillside ecosystems and many millions of pounds' worth of damage to the economies of floodplain areas in India, China, and other countries every year (e.g. Bonavia 1981).

It is generally agreed that both the capacity of the soil moisture reservoir and also the actual amount of water present in this reservoir are typically higher in forest than in grassland. The greater capacity of forest is largely due to the greater depth of penetration of tree roots (Douglass 1967; Oke 1978) and the higher moisture content of the more pervious soil. It is the greater wetness of the soil and the higher water-table under a forest that are responsible for the increased ability of a forested catchment to maintain dry-season flow in streams.

A major question for planners of land use is the amount of disturbance that should be permitted in catchments managed for water protection. McCulloch and Dagg (1962) have pointed out that any grazing by domestic animals inside a forest tends to undermine the hydrological benefits of the forest cover. On Mt Elgon I have observed that the presence of cattle locally inside the forest increases overland flow and exacerbates soil erosion. I have also observed on Mt Elgon that areas of montane grassland which are ungrazed by domestic animals and which are rarely burnt develop soil and vegetation characteristics which largely prevent surface water flow (Hamilton 1982); the effect of cattle grazing and, especially, burning is to reduce drastically the protective cap of litter and to open up bare patches of soil between the grass tussocks, with consequent serious loss of topsoil by surface wash (ibid.). The conclusion is that burning of grass and grazing by domestic stock are inadvisable in catchments managed for water protection.

Concerning agricultural land, there is an added reason for encouraging practices that maintain high levels of soil moisture, since lack of moisture is a major factor limiting crop and pasture growth. There is much evidence from many parts of the world that different techniques of cultivation vary tremendously in their effects on runoff and erosion (e.g. Dunne 1979). Big benefits in water and erosion control can be achieved by the implementation of even small, well-conceived measures. Experimental work in Karamoja has shown that even a brief resting of overgrazed land greatly increases the amount of water which penetrates into the soil (Pereira 1967b).

To summarize, there is no doubt that, in the Ugandan context, tree destruction strongly influences the water cycle and that it probably also has a major impact on the climate. Although little is known quantitatively, all the evidence points to the value of maintaining as high a covering of trees as possible, consistent with using the land for other objectives such as the growing of food crops. I therefore wholeheartedly agree with Nicholson (1929) in his call for forest protection and tree planting, activities which are highly desirable in any case on more immediate economic grounds.

Chapter 6

Forestry in Uganda, 1898-1972

> The Protectorate of Uganda has immense agricultural potentialities the full development of which can only be carried out with the assistance of the handmaid of agriculture—forestry. If the latter's lot be prostitution Uganda will become a sterile solitude. J. W. Nicholson, *The Future of Forestry in Uganda.*

The forestry service was created in 1898 with the appointment of the first Director to the Scientific and Forestry Department of Uganda (Forest Department 1951). The Forestry Department was established as a separate body in 1917 and was renamed the Forest Department in 1927. The first trained foresters arrived in 1921, but it was only in 1929 that forest policy was given serious attention by the Government and the Forest Department was organized into approximately its present form.

The process of acquiring land by the Forest Department was gradual and to a degree unsystematic, and it was not until the 1940s that the boundaries of the forest estate, more or less as they now stand, became established. In Buganda the legal basis for Government involvement in forests was the Uganda Memorandum of Agreement (1900) as amplified and clarified by the Uganda Memorandum of Agreement (Forest) (1907) and the Forests Ordinance (1913). All larger blocks of forest were declared Crown land, coming under government control, but it should be noted that the area of smaller forests on private (*mailo*) land was not inconsiderable. The Toro Agreement (1900), Ankole Agreement (1909), and Bunyoro Agreement (1933) declared all forests in these former kingdoms to be under government control. These various agreements prohibited exploitation of Crown forests without permits, fixed fees, and stipulated items which could be extracted without payment, the latter including firewood and poles for private use. In the absence of centralized and extensive traditional authority, all land in other parts of Uganda was declared Crown land; forest reserves seem to have been set up with a minimum of formality. It should be stressed that not all declared forest reserves consisted (or consist) entirely or even only in part of forest vegetation. Especially in the drier districts, many forest reserves (that is, areas legally reserved for forestry management) were established among savanna vegetation (Figure 5, p. 51).

The earliest commercial activity in the forests of Uganda was the collection of wild rubber from *Landolphia* and *Clitandra* vines and later from the tree *Funtumia elastica*. The first tapping concession was granted in 1902 and rubber production reached a maximum in 1910. However, Uganda rubber came to face severe competition from plantations elsewhere, and exports had virtually ceased by 1919. There was a brief resurgence in wild-rubber collection during the Second World War (Osmaston 1959).

Rubber may be regarded as a minor forest product, and it may be mentioned that at one time or another quite a large number of forest species have been exploited on a small scale. These include species with edible fruits or which yield chemicals of medicinal value, *Raphia farinifera*, the source of raphia fibre, and the climbing palm *Calamus*, used for the manufacture of light furniture and other articles.

Some forests in which the harvesting of timber began early include Munziro (Namalala/Tero) (about 1907), Mabira (1911) and Budongo (1919), in most cases initially by pit-sawing. In the period up to 1926 much of the harvesting was undertaken directly by the Government, an involvement which came to be regarded in retrospect by the Forest Department as unfortunate. Part of the problem was that expenditure on milling tended to exceed income, but, more importantly, the diversion of staff and finance to exploitation seriously set back the development of long-term planning. By the 1930s a policy had evolved which gave the Government the task of regulating the volume and type of timber cut but left extraction and processing in private hands. For example, commercial firms were granted exclusive felling licences over defined parts of the forest estate for prescribed periods of years, licences being given in return for fees payable to the Forest Department per volume of sound timber cut (Forest Department 1934).

Before 1930 very little information was collected on the distribution and other characteristics of Uganda's forests. The only significant exceptions to this generalization were various studies carried out by M. T. Dawe, whose decision to leave Uganda in 1910 was a great set-back to the development of forestry. Dawe discovered the wild rubber tree *Funtumia elastica* in Uganda, at first in Mabira Forest in 1903, and made extensive botanical surveys of forests in the south and west (e.g. Dawe 1906). He also collected some excellent herbarium specimens, which emerged from obscurity in 1930 on the occasion of the removal of the Forest Office to its new quarters in the Old High Court Building in Entebbe—still the Forest Department headquarters. Dawe's specimens were found bundled up in boxes with other early collections, some of which were in a very dilapidated condition. Plants collected by Dawe were in a better state than most, thanks to his excellent collecting and preserving techniques, and many can still be seen at Entebbe where their quality can be appreciated.

Two reports dealing with forestry were written during the 1920s. The earlier one, by Troup (1922), was not adopted by the Government, but many of its suggestions were incorporated in the second report, by Nicholson (1929). Nicholson's report had a major impact on the development of forestry (Forest Department 1930). This excellent and far-sighted document resulted in clarification of the aims of the government forestry service and the establishment of a departmental structure which has persisted basically unaltered until today. Nicholson stressed the fact that forests and trees play important roles in the environment, both in direct economic ways and indirectly by modifying the climate, protecting water supplies, and preventing excessive soil erosion. He believed that Uganda would benefit from a greater forest cover than it had even at that time, and advocated not only widespread forest protection but also major afforestation schemes. Nicholson considered that supplies of firewood, poles, and sawn timber for local consumption in the countryside could best be guaranteed by encouraging tree growing by farmers and by the establishment of small plantations under the control of local administrations. The role of the Forest Department was to safeguard the environment and forest resources on a long-term basis, and among its duties were to be the selection of reserves, the demarcation of their boundaries, the writing of legislation to permit forest conservation, research, preparation of working plans, exploitation, and afforestation. It was advocated that the number of professional staff in the Forest Department be increased to eighteen, an establishment which was not attained until 1946 (Forest Department 1951).

Many of Nicholson's suggestions regarding the aims of the Forest Department were incorporated in an official Forest Policy Statement in 1948, in which two objectives of the Forest Department were given, as follows:

1. To reserve in perpetuity, for the benefit of the present inhabitants of Uganda and of posterity, sufficient land (either already forested or capable of afforestation) to maintain climatic conditions suitable for agriculture, to preserve water supplies, to provide forest produce for agricultural, industrial and domestic supplies, and to maintain soil stability in areas where the land is liable to deterioration if put to other uses.

2. To manage this forest estate to obtain the best returns on its capital value and the expenses of management, in so far as such returns are consistent with the primary aims set out above.

A significant change in the Forest Policy Statement of 1948 compared with the forest policy advocated earlier by Nicholson was the down-grading of the value of protective forestry (for climatic modification, etc.) in recognition of the pressing immediate demands of agriculture. In the words of the Forest Policy Statement, 'because of Uganda's dependence on agriculture, the rapid development of the country, and the continuing increase of its population, it is necessary to limit the size of the forest estate to the minimum area which will achieve the primary aims of management.' Minimum is the key word here. Although there could have been no reliable method of determining the size of the minimum area in the meaning of the Statement, nevertheless a 'minimum area' was calculated for each administrative district; when the actual area of legally protected forest reached or exceeded this amount, then the district was declared to be adequately forested. Minimum areas were calculated using figures for wood consumption per head and the sizes of district populations, and there was also an initial aim to place 10% of the land area of Uganda under forest. Figures were adjusted between districts to compensate for low production or high land pressure.

Legislation establishing forest reserves under district administrations was enacted in 1938 and 1947. These new 'Local Forest Reserves' were expected to be small and numerous and to cater for local demands. Their creation was not expected to detract from the value of 'Central Forest Reserves', which were usually larger and were supposed to serve regional needs. In addition to the task of looking after Central Forest Reserves, the central government Forest Department was expected to continue with its educational, advisory, and research functions (though in practice the encouragement of tree-growing by farmers came to be undertaken largely by the Department of Agriculture). The establishment of Local Forest Reserves was in line with the Government's Post-War Development Plan, which laid particular stress on the provision of small areas of natural forest or plantations to supply wood products to the rural community on a permanent basis (Forest Department 1955).

During the late 1940s and early 1950s the Forest Department expressed concern about the poor management of the not inconsiderable area of privately owned forest in Buganda. These forests were a major source of the country's timber (44% in 1949). The response of the Department was the 'Buganda Dedication Scheme', giving owners the opportunity to lease their forests to the Buganda Government for a period of 99 years (Sangster 1951a and b). Leased forests would be managed by the local forest service to give maximum sustainable timber production, and the owner would receive 75% of the profits. The scheme was not a success, probably because of the highly emotive nature of land issues in Buganda, including a general suspicion of Government's intentions. Another scheme tried out at this time and which also failed was a plan for the establishment of communally-owned village forests.

The period 1930 to 1960 was one of considerable achievement in the evolution of methods of cropping the natural forests for timber, a field in which Uganda came to be recognized as a leader among tropical countries. Studies in forest ecology were initiated by Eggeling in the 1930s, forming the basis of management techniques later followed up by Dawkins and others. Eggeling re-organized the Forest Department Herbarium, and in 1940 completed his book *The Indigenous Trees of the Uganda Protectorate*, a notable achievement. The first research plots for determining the growth characteristics of natural forests in different places and under different treatments were established in 1933; the number of these had risen to 267 by 1960.

Natural forests in Ugand tend to contain a rather large number of tree species, of various timber values. In recognition of this, the Forest Department devised a system of grading species into classes according to current worth, species being occasionally shifted between categories in response to increases in knowledge, industrial developments, or changes in fashion. Royalties payable by sawmillers or pit-sawyers varied between timber classes, and the department tried to devise methods of management which would increase the numbers of the more desirable species. Large-scale operations were initiated in Budongo and the Mengo forests in the late 1930s, enrichment at first being pursued by the line-planting of nursery-grown specimens of valuable trees, such as *Entandrophragma, Khaya,* and *Maesopsis*, after exploitation of an initial timber crop (Philip 1962). Following on from about 1945 this technique was replaced by one of compensatory planting to supplement natural regeneration. This method was adopted both because of a labour shortage and because it was felt that natural regeneration was adequate to ensure a reasonable second crop over large parts of the forests.

A major problem of forest management has been that some of the commonest species of tall tree, such as *Cynometra alexandri* and *Parinari excelsa*, have been of low commercial value. Arboricides were introduced to kill these and other weed species in 1954 and soon were being used on a large scale to simulate heavy felling (Hughes and Lang Brown 1962). One disadvantage quickly became apparent, namely that the crashing down of dead branches and whole trees could cause severe damage to young individuals of desirable species trying to grow up beneath them.

Techniques for the management of the natural forests for timber production were eventually clarified with the general adoption of a monocyclic felling plan (Dawkins 1958; Philip 1962). This called for the conversion of a

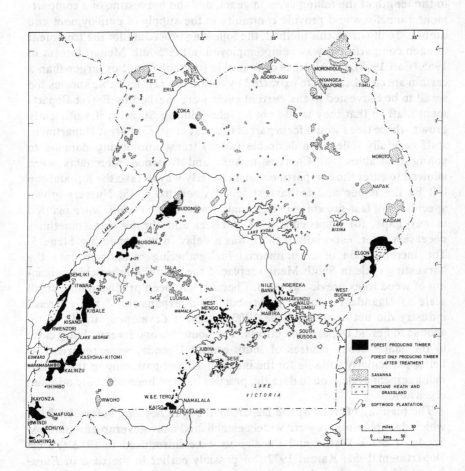

Figure 5. Forest reserves in Uganda

The map is based on that in the *Atlas of Uganda,* 2nd. edition (1967). Only a few minor
changes to the legal limits of reserves occurred between 1967 and 1982.

forest into a mosaic of even-aged crops, each part of the mosaic being harvested at regular intervals (of the order of 50 to 100 years). Where practicable, forests were to be divided into compartments equal in number to the length of the felling cycle in years, and the harvesting of a compartment annually would provide continuity in the supply of employment and timber. To illustrate this method, the following procedure for the treatment of each compartment was being employed in the South Mengo forests in 1965 (Earl 1968). (1) All trees of desirable (valuable) species larger than a certain specified size were extracted by the miller. (2) Desirable species too small to be harvested in the current cycle were marked by Forest Department staff so that they would not be felled during Stage 3; if sufficiently grown, these trees would form part of the next crop. (3) Forest Department staff carefully felled non-desirable (weed) trees, minimizing damage to young desirables. (4) Charcoal-makers and firewood merchants were allowed to enter the compartment in an orderly way to take the lop-and-top left by the miller and to harvest felled weed trees. (5) Nursery-grown specimens of fast-growing species, mainly *Maesopsis eminii*, were planted in any gaps. (6) Some cutting of climbers and shrubs was sometimes necessary later, especially if there was a delay in implementing Stage 5. The incorporation of a commercial fuel-gathering component into the harvesting cycle in South Mengo replaced the wasteful arboricide poisoning of weed trees previously used. Charcoal had been produced on a small scale in Uganda for many years, but rapid expansion of the charcoal industry did not occur until the 1960s, when it developed largely in response to Forest Department efforts. The South Mengo forests, lying close to the major urban centres of south central Uganda, were regarded as being particularly suitable for the inclusion of fuel-gathering in the forest-management cycle, and to date the practice has not been officially adopted elsewhere.

The planting of trees by the Department began not long before 1908, by which date plantations were widely established near government stations. Seeds of Black Wattle and *Eucalyptus* were introduced in 1912 (Forest Department 1951; Karani 1972), or possibly earlier in the case of *Eucalyptus* (Karani, personal communication), but an indigenous tree, nsambya (*Markhamia platycalyx*), was the main species used in the early years. *Mvule* (*Chlorophora. excelsa*), which was one of the most important early timber trees, was harvested mainly from cultivated areas and derived savanna in Busoga, where its lack of regeneration was a cause of concern. Much effort was put into the establishment of experimental plantations in Busoga in the 1930s, but these met with a singular lack of success (Eggeling 1948a). However, plantations of *mvule*, as well as one of the mahoganies (*Khaya grandifolia*), thrived in Acholi and Lango, possibly, in the case of *mvule*, because of a reduced incidence of the gall-fly (*Phytolyma*) and other pests. Meanwhile *Eucalyptus* has spread widely through Uganda and has become the main source of poles and firewood in some areas. The first softwood plantation was established in Kigezi in 1942.

In 1967 the forest services run by district administrations were absorbed into the centrally organized Forest Department. The adjectives 'local' and 'central' now lost their meanings when applied to forest reserves and were no longer officially used. This amalgamation was not due in any direct sense to considerations of forestry or environmental welfare, but was rather a part of the general shift towards political centralization which followed Ugandan independence. According to the Forest Department Report for 1964—1968, abolition of local forestry services was welcomed by most people interested in forestry on the ground that it would ensure efficiency and rationality in the development of forest resources. However, no detailed reasons are given in support of this statement, which can be sympathetically regarded as an inevitable one for a department of government under the prevailing circumstances. Nicholson (1929) had originally argued that responsibility for the provision of village-level wood requirements should rest at the local level, on the ground that local governments were in a much better position to look after a large number of small reserves, that costs would be less, and that local administrative involvement would help to generate public interest in forestry. Nicholson maintained that local administrations could maintain the necessary level of technical skill. Nicholson's belief in the economic advantages of local administration might be regarded as vindicated by the decision of the Forest Department following the 1967 centralization to relinquish some of the smaller forests (up to about 20 ha), which had been acquired from local governments on the grounds of economic inviability.

Some idea of the performance of local forest administrations during their period of existence can be gleaned from Forest Department publications, but it is unfortunate that all forest records in the Buganda archives seem to have been destroyed during the violent events of 1966. At its peak, in the middle of 1966, the total area of Local Forest Reserves stood at 306 000 ha. a substantial figure which may be compared with the 1 159 000 ha of the Central Forest estate. Local Forest Reserves included natural forests, woodlands, and plantations. Active work was concentrated on the development of small softwood plantations. The Buganda Government was particularly energetic in acquiring new forest reserves, adding no less than 137 270 ha in about the last two years of its existence, and some of the other local governments also showed some enthusiasm for forestry. However, a few, such as Lango and Karamoja, made very little progress. The complaint of the Forest Department (1968) that Buganda's forestry service had become unco-operative after independence was clearly not due to a lack of interest in forestry as such, but should rather be seen as part of the wider struggle for political power which was a feature of this period. For example, the Buganda Government interpreted the Buganda Agreement of 1961 as meaning that after independence (in 1962) all forest reserves in Buganda, whether central or local, would be transferred to itself, a point of view which not surprisingly proved to be at variance with that of the Central Government.

On the subject of legislation, the present authority of the Forest Department derives from the Forest Act of 1964 and a number of subsequent statutory instruments, the most important being Number 151 of 1967 centralizing the administration of Local Forest Reserves. Forest reserves stand on Crown land, which became public land at independence, and the Public Lands Act of 1969 stated that all public land is vested in the Uganda Land Commission. (A land-reform decree in 1975 nationalized all rural land, and consequently all rural land is now public land.) Section 48 of the Public Lands Act states that nothing in the Act shall affect the law relating to forestry as it affects public land, which implies that degazetting is necessary before the transfer of forest reserves to other uses by the Land Commission. Routine administration of the Forest Department is covered by Standing Orders, last revised in 1970 (Forest Department 1970).

While it is true that the period 1930 to 1970 was marked by general progress in forestry, there were indications by the 1960s that the planting programme needed acceleration to prevent the development of a serious shortage in the supply of sawn timber and other tree products. This is the view contained in three reports on forestry development produced by UNESCO (1964), the FAO (1967) and Lockwood Consultants (1973), the latter prepared in conjunction with the Uganda Forest Department on behalf of the Canadian International Development Agency. These reports examined the current consumption of tree products and gave projections of future requirements, making various assumptions about changes in population, income per head, and degree of urbanization. There is much uncertainty about current levels of utilization, particularly for firewood and poles, and even greater doubt about future trends, but even so all reports agree in predicting big increases in demand for all products. The FAO figures for current consumption per person are given in Table 11, where they may be compared wih some Forest Department estimates. Present and projected countryside demands according to Lockwood (1973) are shown in Table 12. The three reports recommend that extensive areas of natural forest should continue to be managed for timber production and that much of the extra demand anticipated should be met by expansion of softwood plantations. Lockwood estimated that the 9000 ha of softwoods already extant needed to be expanded to 30 000 ha by the year A.D. 2000 to

Table 11. Consumption per head per year of wood products in Uganda (tons)

	FAO estimates for 1959– 61 period	Forest Department estimates for 1965– 68 period
Fuelwood (including charcoal)	1.48	1.29
Roundwood	0.10	0.092
Sawn wood	0.0126	0.0167
Paper/paperboard	0.00038 tons	3.5 (Shs.)

The FAO paper/paperboard estimate is for 1960– 62.

Table 12a. Estimated production (1970) and projected demand (1980–2000) for timber, plywood, and matches according to Lockwood (1973)

Year	1970	1980	1990	2000
Sawn timber	71 793	101 104	185 190	339 212
Plywood	14 440	21 800	33 400	52 230
Matches	16 853	29 348	43 160	43 160
Total	103 086	152 252	261 750	435 602

Figures in cubic metres.

Table 12b. Estimated production (1970) and projected demand (1980–2000) for fuelwood, charcoal, and poles according to Lockwood (1973)

Year	1970	1980	2000
i. For use in the subsistence sector of the economy			
Fuelwood	10 000 000	14 000 000	25 000 000
Poles	700 000	1 000 000	1 750 000
ii. For use in the monetary sector of the economy			
Firewood	560 000	560 000	0
Charcoal	50 000	100 000	400 000
Poles	13 376	29 000	80 000

The units are cubic metres, except for charcoal (tonnes).

meet medium-term sawn-timber requirements. The emphasis on softwoods follows current forestry practices in temperate countries, but softwoods may not be particularly suitable for Ugandan environments. Their main advantage is said to be their relatively high productivity, but none of the reports seriously considers either whether part of the projected demand for timber could be met by plantations of non-coniferous trees or whether management systems in natural forests could be changed to achieve higher useful productivity. Possible deleterious edaphic consequences of coniferous forestry are also not discussed.

A small paper mill, named PAPCO and using pulp brought in from Kenya, had been established in Jinja by the early 1960s. In view of the high cost of pulp importation and the inadequate size of PAPCO, the Lockwood Report (1973) recommended that a paper-and-pulp plant be established in Uganda of a size sufficient for the country's needs. I understand that the plan called for small satellite pulping mills scattered near plantations throughout the country to feed a central paper plant at Jinja. It is interesting that as recently as 1964 UNESCO had regarded the demand for paper products even throughout the whole of eastern Africa as too small to justify the construction of a mill, and it is presumed that the change in advice reflected either a transformation in the economics of paper milling or the increasing isolation of Uganda within East Africa as the East African Community fell apart and regional planning for economic development could no longer be assumed. Lockwood recommended the planting of 30 000 ha of softwood to produce the raw material for pulping, so that the total softwood estate proposed for the year 2000 would be 60 000 ha.

Although uncertainty surrounds the exact quantities involved, there is no doubt that much more wood is used as fuel and as poles than in more processed forms such as sawn timber. Estimates of the ratio of wood used for fuel, poles and sawn timber (by volume) are of the order of 100:7:1 and Table 12 shows just how massive are Lockwood's projections of future fuelwood, charcoal, and pole requirements. Thus it is unclear why neither UNESCO nor Lockwood envisaged much problem with the future supply of fuel or poles. Lockwood rather casually suggests that the use of fuel should be monitored and local plantations established before shortages develop, but no detailed plans are proposed and the suggestion has not been implemented.

During the late 1960s the Norwegian Agency for International Development (NORAD) became involved in forestry activities in Uganda, especially with the implementation of the FAO/UNESCO softwood expansion scheme and with the development of forestry education at Nyabyeya Forest College in Budongo Forest and at Makerere University. A sizeable body of information on the growing of softwoods was already available from the many experimental plots which had been established during earlier years, and therefore NORAD was able to move straight into large-scale planting. A major site was Katugo at mile 60 on the Kampala-Gulu Road, *Pinus caribaea* being the main species used. A Department of Forestry was opened at Makerere University in 1970 under a 5-year inter-governmental agreement, NORAD paying for staff, equipment, and transportation. The objective was to produce graduate foresters for much of eastern Africa, and the pioneer class of students hailed from no fewer than six countries. Practical classes were held throughout East Africa.

Forest policy came under review in the early 1970s and the Forest Policy Statement of 1948 was succeeded by a Statement of Forestry Policy issued by the Forest Department in 1971 and by the informal adoption by senior foresters in 1974 of some policy proposals contained in the Lockwood Report (1973). The 1971 Statement and Lockwood Report differ in emphasis, and it is not clear which has governmental priority. The 1971 Statement of Forest Policy states that the objectives of the Forest Department are:

1. To reserve adequate land as forest estate so as to ensure:
   i. a sustained production of timber and other forest products for the needs of the country, and where feasible for export also;
   ii. protection of water catchments, soils, wildlife and amenity of land.
2. To develop that estate so as to obtain maximum economic return to the country.
3. To ensure efficient conversion of wood and wood products, so as to reduce waste.
4. To carry out extension services aimed at:
   i. helping farmers, organizations and other people to grow and protect their own trees;
   ii. educating the public about the role of forestry and forest industries for their welfare;
   iii. advising industries and users of wood on suitability and availability of various uses.

Lockwood Consultants (1973) state that forest policy is the sum total of all government actions and policies which affect forests, adding that what goes by the name of forest policy is really forest-management policy. Be that as it may, Lockwood recommends that the following should be the main objectives of forest policy:

1. To ensure the supply of raw material for direct use, or for processing by industry, both in the present and with provision for the future.
2. To provide employment opportunities in those areas where unemployment is at unacceptable levels.
3. To capture the returns to the Nation from the natural forest resource resulting from the utilization of the remaining natural high forest areas.

4. To recover all costs, interest charges and returns for risks associated with the planning and development of afforestation and enrichment planting programmes.

When senior foresters adopted these proposals in 1974, they agreed to add a further statement concerning extension services.

In comparison with the 1948 Forest Policy Statement these new policy statements show an increased emphasis on the direct monetary value of forest products and a downgrading of protective forestry. This is particularly true of Lockwood, in which the wider values of forests, for example as regulators of water supplies, are barely considered. Lockwood declares that protective forestry should be left to the common sense of the individual forest officer; to quote: 'There are other secondary objectives such as the protection of water catchments, soils, wildlife and amenity of land. These however cannot be measured and are dependant on responsible behaviour by Departmental officials in their provision.'

To summarize the period up the the early 1970s, two phases in the history of government intervention in forests can be recognized. Up to 1929 the Forest Department was very small and much of its effort was put into direct forest exploitation rather than into long-term planning and the acquisition and development of a national forest estate. Following re-organization in 1929 the Department's aims were much more clearly defined and there followed a period of active forestry. Techniques evolved for managing tropical forests for timber production were internationally acclaimed. During the 1960s the belief spread that an acceleration of the tree-planting programme was needed to meet future requirements for sawn timber and paper products, and a start was made on expanding the area of coniferous plantations.

Chapter 7

Forestry in Uganda, 1972-1982

> It is . . . only a matter of time before a national shortage of land becomes a real problem. Moreover, in certain areas of the country there is a menacing confrontation between competitive land uses, whose resolution requires immediate attention. *National Report on the Human Environment* (1972)

The period since about 1973 has witnessed a serious reduction in the extent of forest in Uganda, a decline in the number of trees outside forests, and major erosion of the effectiveness of the Forest Department. The period has also been characterized by a shortage of information, making it very difficult to gain a reliable nationwide perspective. At the local level, people from many parts of the country complain of a shortage of wood and there are indications that the environment is deteriorating in other ways as a result of reduction in the numbers of trees. Despite the limitations of the evidence, the overall impression at the time of writing in 1982 is that depletion of the forestry resource is a cause of grave concern.

A major development was the return of Government to direct involvement in extractive forest industries. At the beginning of 1972 nearly all the major sawmills in Uganda were owned by people originating from the Indian subcontinent and, when 'Asians' were expelled from the country later in that year, the ownership of these mills 'fell vacant'. Urgent action was needed to keep the mills running and so a new section of the Forest Department known as the Ugandan Government Sawmills Project was created to act as the managing organization. Many foresters moved into this section. In 1974 this body was itself dissolved and its assets were acquired by a new parastatal body standing outside the Forest Department, the Wood Industries Corporation (WICO). The nationalization of the sawmills was welcomed by many foresters (e.g. Kizito 1973), and it was widely envisaged that exports of timber would soon come to rank with those of coffee and cotton as earners of foreign exchange.

Twenty-one sawmills were originally acquired by WICO and in general they were in a reasonable state of repair at the time of nationalization. One by one the sawmills fell out of production, until by 1980 only two, **Budongo** and Kiira, were operating at anything like full capacity. A further sawmill, Kasenene, occasionally managed to produce a few planks. The Hoima and Kalinzu sawmills had been burnt down. Although considered when founded as likely to become a major generator of income, WICO has proved to be a financial burden rather than an asset. Royalties for trees felled have never been paid to the Forest Department and large sums of money are owed to banks, particularly the Uganda Commercial Bank. The woes of WICO have contributed to a massive increase in pit-sawing, much of it unlicensed. Reasons given for the failure of WICO include a lack of spare parts for machinery and shortage of technical and management expertise. Also, the founding of WICO resulted in much increased administrative costs, associated with the new headquarters of the organization in Kampala.

In December 1980 the Government announced that all but six of WICO's sawmills were to go into private ownership. Outstanding debts were retained entirely by WICO. The sawmills remaining with WICO were Budongo, Kiira, Bugoma, Kalinzu, Lendu, and Mafuga. I understand that at present (June 1982) The last four of these mills are also in the process of denationalization.

The relationship between these changes of ownership and the export of timber is of interest. When established, WICO was authorized by government decree as the sole legal exporter of timber. Under this legal definition, there have been no exports of timber since 1978, when the value of exports amounted to a mere 3500 US dollars. However, it is said that there is an illegal export trade, mainly to Kenya. Moreover, recent government policy has attempted to increase exports by granting individual export licences. Most recently, in 1981, an agreement was reached with the Government of India to export 100 tons of high-grade timber per month in part exchange for imports of manufactured goods. The origin of this deal, which has not to my knowledge been implemented, may be a feeling by some government officials that Uganda is rich in valuable timber, though actually the amount of timber which can be exported on a sustainable basis, if any, is an unknown quantity.

In April 1973 the Norwegian Government decided to withdraw aid from the country. Forestry was affected in various ways. For example, the Norwegian staff at Makerere, together with all continuing students, moved across to Kenyatta College of the University of Nairobi in Kenya, where the Norwegians continued with the course for a further year. (Norwegian-assisted higher education in forestry has since been transferred to Morogoro, Tanzania, where a few Ugandans have attended as postgraduates.) With the departure of the Norwegians, Makerere was galvanized into hastily assembling a replacement forestry staff and, much to the University's credit, the department remained open and has continued to operate ever since. The Forest Department at Makerere was originally designed to serve a large part of eastern Africa, but events have forced it to become very much a national rather than an international institution and it has received no foreign students since 1978; during recent years it has had only one non-Ugandan member of staff. About 80 people had graduated from this department to 1981, the majority going into the Forest Department, which today employs more graduates than at any time in the past (about 170 in 1982). Before 1982 all graduates who wished to do so had no difficulty in obtaining employment either in the Forest Department or WICO, but 1982 was a bad year because of a financial crisis resulting in a complete lack of new government forestry posts. For the first time in Uganda, graduates in forestry joined the long line of the educated unemployed. Unlike graduates in some other disciplines, such as medicine and education, those in forestry are unlikely to be able to find relief from the economic and political problems of their country by easily securing jobs in their chosen profession beyond its boundaries.

Since about 1972 there has been serious erosion of the Forest Department estate. On paper the gazetted area of Forest Department land in 1978 stood at 15 280 000 ha, including about 732 000 ha of savanna woodland and 24 000 ha of plantations (10 000 ha of which were softwoods). Although any figure must be regarded as a wild guess, some forestry officials consider that as much as 300 000 ha of this land had moved out of departmental control over the 10-year period up to early 1982, giving an annual compound rate of loss of roughly 2%. At most, only a very small part of the lost land has been degazetted, so that theoretically the Forest Department still retains ownership; in a few cases the transfer of land is official, but most of the loss is due to illegal agricultural encroachment.

Encroachment and other illegal activities are not new forestry problems in Uganda, but their scale over the past ten years is quite different from that which prevailed previously. It is clear from Forest Department reports that illegality was not a serious problem before the 1960s, and it is convenient to trace its growth from the low level prevailing at the beginning of that decade. Taking the administrative year 1959—1960, illegality of all types was minimal outside Buganda; inside Buganda some theft of poles from plantations was reported, over 60 trees were known to have been felled illegally, and there was a small amount of settlement in Mabira Forest, where it was encouraged by a loophole in the law (Forest Department 1960). There is mention of attempted violence on a minor scale against Forest Department staff in Buganda. The 1964 Annual Report shows illegality to be still at a low level, though increasing. Violence against Forest Department personnel had by now been reported from other parts of the country in addition to Buganda. Encroachment was still low. The situation had deteriorated further by 1968, the Report for the 1964—1968 period stating that theft of poles and firewood was common near towns generally and that encroachment was present in various parts of the country. At the time of the most recent Forest Department Report, in 1974, theft and encroachment were mentioned as being major problems.

The following paragraphs outline the recent history and current status of forests and forest reserves in Uganda. In the virtual absence of any published information for the last decade, this section has been pieced together from discussions with interested parties, supplemented by some fairly detailed reports by a few of my students for particular localities and occasional visits to forests by myself. I have also been fortunate to receive a briefing on the results of an aerial survey of forests in western Uganda undertaken in April 1982, from Kibale Forest southwards (Malpas, personal communication). Additionally, there is a very useful report by Van Orsdol (1983) on the encroachment problem in southern Kibale Forest. Independent studies by Carvalho (1982) and myself of changes in forest extent visible on satellite images have also been of some help. Although many of the statements given here have been confirmed from more than one source, there is necessarily an element of uncertainty concerning some of the reported developments.

Beginning with the savanna reserves of the north-west, sixteen square miles of Mt Kei were 'cleared' by a friend of President Amin during the latter's period of office. Access to this area is not easy at present, but it is reported that the man in question fled to the Sudan after Amin's downfall. A similar case of encroachment occurred in Eria Forest Reserve and the person responsible is also said to have left the country. Further to the east, Agoro-Agu Forest Reserve was allocated by the Governor of Northern Province to various government departments and private individuals in 1975, the Forest Department itself receiving a share of its own land. This action was apparently a response to President Amin's call to double agricultural production following the departure of the 'Asians' and the declaration of an 'Economic War'. At present Agoro-Agu has reportedly been recovered by the Forest Department, with the exception of an area carrying a Prisons Department farm.

Two plantations near Gulu, known as Abera and Opit, were badly burnt in about March/April 1982. Abera had been planted by the Forest Department, but had been transferred to the National Tobacco Corporation during the 1970s, coming under the administration of a local co-operative society. It is believed that this forest was fired maliciously, probably because of resentment by some local people of the new ownership. Plantations around Pakwach, in the south of West Nile, were also extensively damaged by fire in 1975, reportedly by accident.

Moving down the western side of Uganda, the first natural high forest about which I have information is Budongo and its neighbourhood. This area, particularly that lying to the south-west of Masindi town, is one for which I have a report from one of my students. The bulk of Budongo Forest is believed to be little affected by encroachment, but there is said to have been recent heavy settlement along the western edge by people from West Nile and Zaire. This area cannot be visited in safety by Forest Department officials. The south-eastern margin of Budongo is also somewhat eroded. The student reports that many small forest patches to the south of Budongo (many not actually forest reserves) have been or are in the process of being destroyed (Figure 6). He also says that near Masindi two streams, the Kasokwa and the Namosoro, have tended to dry up since forest in their catchments was replaced by cultivation.

Bugoma and Itwara Forest Reserves are believed to be substantially intact, possibly because of a relatively low local population. On the other hand, recent aerial reconnaisance has shown Semliki Forest Reserve to be more seriously damaged by encroachment than any of the other large forests in western Uganda (Malpas, personal communication). There is a strip of contained encroachment going back many years running along the Bundibujio-Fort Portal Road. A more serious problem now is widespread clearance deep within the forest. This probably dates back to the time after the Liberation War of 1978–9. Ground-based reports of encroachment in Rwenzori Forest Reserve have not been confirmed by recent aerial examination (Malpas, personal communication).

The southern part of Kibale Forest Reserve and nearby Kisangi Forest Reserve are the sites of two of the earliest major encroachments in Uganda; clearing by Bakiga immigrants started in 1971 or 1972 in Kibale and a year or two later in Kisangi. It is probable that all of Kisangi has now been felled. The 1982 aerial survey showed that encroachment over much of the western part of southern Kibale has been very heavy, but that a strip of forest still survived near the Dura River on the east (Malpas, personal communication). Van Orsdol (1983) has carried out a detailed examination of the encroachment problem in southern Kibale; this study included extensive field work between June and December 1982. Van Orsdol has estimated from census data that about 7000 people were settled in the forest in 1980. By 1982, 97 km^2 of Kibale Forest Reserve had been disturbed by encroachers. Today the immigrants in southern Kibale are well established and have acquired schools, health clinics, and an officially recognized hierarchy of chiefs. Various government agencies have therefore accepted the fact of encroachment, but the Forest Department says that it still plans to evict the settlers and to re-establish the area under its

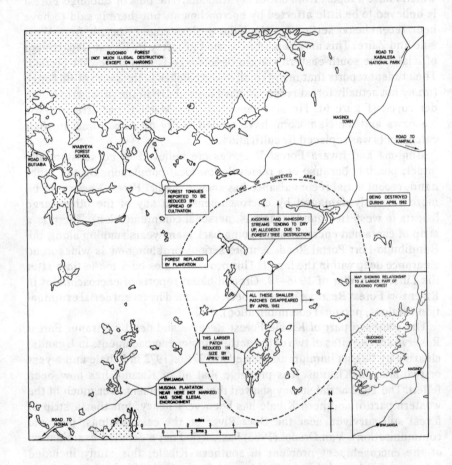

Figure 6. *Recent forest destruction to the south-east of Budongo Forest*

Forest distribution on the baseline map as in 1960

authority. In northern and central Kibale a total of about 8 km² is known to have been taken illegally by cultivators and there are reports of threatened violence against Forest Department staff who have attempted to evict the squatters (Butynski, personal communication). Aerial survey has confirmed some forest clearance near the south-eastern boundary of the northern block, but the northern boundary seems to be substantially intact. The healthy state of the latter can probably be attributed to the existence of a protective fringe of tea estates. For a number of years Kibale Forest has been the site of a forest-ecology research station under the auspices of the New York Zoological Society, and some of the resident foreign scientists have given their active support to the Forest Department in trying to prevent illegal activities within the forest.

Observations from the air (Malpas, personal communication) and reports from the ground suggest that there is little encroachment in Kasyoha-Kitomi, Kalinzu, and Maramagambo Forests. However, some illegal cultivation is said to be present in Kalinzu, and the increasing population along the south-eastern edge of Maramagambo is a cause for concern.

In Kigezi, reports indicate that Bwindi and Kayonza Forest Reserves have suffered little from encroachment and this is confirmed by aerial examination (Malpas, personal communication). The aerial survey did however show that non-reserve forest patches which were present to the west of Kayonza in the early 1960s have been completely cleared. Some farmers who settled in the neck between the Bwindi and Kayonza Forests departed after being served with eviction notices. These forests are major sources of timber, not only for consumption locally in Uganda, but also for smuggling into forest-deficient Rwanda. There is much illegal pit-sawing. There is some encroachment in Ihimbo, a small reserve north of Kayonza. In Mafuga Forest Reserve, which is one of the largest softwood plantations in Uganda, the remaining unplanted area of 1300 ha is alleged to have been illegally allocated to farmers in 1979—1980 by a forest officer.

In Echuya Forest Reserve land was made available in 1975—1976 to the Department of Agriculture for an experimental wheat and barley project with promised financial assistance from a foreign source; clearing of the natural vegetation (bamboo) started in 1978. With the fall of President Amin, this assistance failed to materialize, and the land is not being used today (1982) for the purpose originally intended. Indeed, the land, which has an area of about 300 ha, is under 'normal' crops and therefore looks like an encroachment. The Forest Department plans repossession. Also in Echuya, a 5-year permit to graze cattle on the swamp in the centre of the forest was granted to an individual in 1978. The terms of the permit allow grazing on some of the grassland which is locally present between the swamp and the forest margin. My observations show that there are considerable areas of cultivation associated with this farm, which has all the appearance of turning into a mixed enterprise. Perhaps encouraged by these activities, other farmers have established small unauthorized patches of crops near the swamp and two large clearings, one about 80 ha in size, have been made deep within the forest. These have occurred since 1979 and are alleged to be the work of a forest officer.

Mgahinga Forest, well known as one of the only two sites in Uganda for gorilla, is a reserve which was reduced from an original gazetted area of 34 km^2 to 23 km^2 in 1950 as a result of population pressure (Donisthorpe 1959). Today there is some agricultural encroachment along the western border close to the border with Zaire and a recent recommendation is that this part of the reserve should be excised (Malpas, personal communication). There is said to be illegal cutting of bamboo and grazing of stock within the reserve.

In Buganda it is reported that there is little agricultural encroachment in West Mengo or in the lake-side forest reserves such as Jubiya and Malabigambo near Masaka, although there is much illegal felling. Luunga and Tala savanna Forest Reserves in Singo County have been heavily settled since 1980 by immigrants from Kigezi. Of all the forest reserves in Buganda, however, Mabira Forest is regarded by the Forest Department as their biggest headache. Until 1953 the presence of the *mbwa* fly (*Simulium*) was responsible for keeping down interference and, although some encroachment was reported in about 1960, at the end of the 1960s encroachment was not regarded as a major problem (Earl 1971). The collapse of forest protection seems to date from the mid-1970s, when it is alleged that the Minister of Local Administration encouraged settlement in the reserve, reputedly in response to the Government's call to 'double agricultural production'. An unusual difficulty for forestry officials in this case was that some of the land had been appropriated by members of the investigative police organization known as the State Research Bureau, who were armed. Today about 2000 people are settled in north-east Mabira. There are many reports of agricultural encroachment and uncontrolled charcoal burning in other parts of the forest, which has been described as looking like a hollow shell from the air. The Forest Department has recently (1982) granted 5-year farming permits to squatters in the forest.

An interesting development which came to my attention in 1982 was the fact that farmers in a village near Entebbe had been trying to stop charcoal-burners from operating in their area because of a belief that tree destruction causes climatic developments harmful to agriculture.

There are numerous encroachment problems in Busoga. Walulumbu Forest Reserve near Jinja was lost between 1967 and 1970 through encroachment; the Department retains only 119 ha of experimental plots.

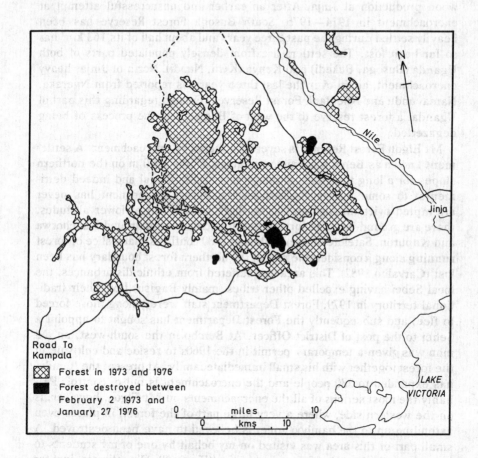

*Figure 7. Mabira Forest: retreat of forest between 1973 and 1976 as visible on
LANDSAT images*

Note: much forest clearance has occurred since 1976.

Half of Bukaleba Forest Reserve was transferred to the Ministry of Animal Resources in 1975; the remaining part has recently been very heavily encroached, which is regarded by some foresters as being exceptionally unfortunate since it was intended to use the land to raise softwoods for plywood production at Jinja. After an earlier and unsuccessful attempt at encroachment in 1974—1975, South Busoga Forest Reserve has been heavily settled during the past three years and about half of its 163 km² has so far been lost. The settlers are from densely populated parts of both Uganda (Busoga, Bukedi) and Kenya (Kisii, Nandi). North of Jinja, heavy encroachment, again over the last three years, is reported from Ngereka, Namavundu and Nile Bank Forest Reserves. Finally, regarding this part of Uganda, a forest reserve to the west of Bugwe is in the process of being degazetted.

Mt Elgon Forest Reserve is severely affected by encroachment. A settlement known as Benet has existed at about 2750—3000 m on the northern slopes for a long time and, although technically illegal and indeed detrimental to some forestry objectives, the Forest Department has never attempted eviction. Also on the northern slopes, but at lower altitudes, there are ground-based reports of recent encroachment around Kapchorwa and Kapuron. Satellite imagery taken in 1980 confirms that a slice of forest running along a considerable part of the northern forest boundary has been lost (Carvalho 1982). This area has suffered from ethnic disturbances, the local Sebei having expelled other tribes (mainly Bagisu) from their traditional territory in 1979. Forest Department staff were among those forced to flee, and subsequently the Forest Department has sought to appoint a Sebei to the post of District Officer. At Bumbo in the south-west, an old man was given a temporary permit in the 1960s to reside and cultivate in the forest together with his small immediate family. At present the 'family' has expanded to 230 people and the encroachment is out of control. Probably the most serious of all the encroachments on Mt Elgon, however, is on the western side, where a very large part of the forest, in places even extending up to the bamboo zone, is believed to have been destroyed. A small part of this area was visited on my behalf by one of my students to investigate the extent of forest destruction (Figure 8). His estimate, just for the limited area which he managed to inspect, is a loss of about 82 km² of forest and the involvement of five to seven thousand farmers. According to my student, encroachment started in the Bumasifwa region in 1979 and spread on to the west-running Nkokonjeru Ridge in 1980. One immediate cause was the influx of Bagisu refugees from Sebei, exacerbating an already serious population problem. By April 1982 cultivation extended in places up to the base of the bamboo zone, which itself was being widely used for grazing cattle. The student says that the rainy seasons near the forest boundary have recently been starting late and have become less reliable, and reports that local farmers attribute these developments to forest destruction.

In Karamoja there is reported to be illegal cultivation and grazing of domestic animals in Kadam Forest Reserve, but Mt Moroto Forest Reserve is said to be less affected. Timu and Morongole Forest Reserves in northern Karamoja are virtually inaccessible to Forest Department officials at present because of local insecurity.

It is clear that the Forest Department has lost much of its former effectiveness (see also FAO 1981). Today the organization is short of money and equipment, and morale is low. All working plans are out of date and, partly because of a shortage of paper, few records are kept of forestry activities. Boundaries often remain uncleared and supervision is inadequate. No improvement work in natural forests has been carried out since about 1974, and it is said that not a single tree has been planted by the Department since 1975. Research is more or less in abeyance and there is little or no survey or inventory work. The extension service seems to be almost totally ineffective, and in practice, if not in theory, the Department has failed to encourage farmers to plant trees. There is corruption within the Department and its work has occasionally been further under-cut by politicians adopting the populist line that land is 'for the people' and should not be 'alienated' as forest reserves. The authority of the Forest Department depends very much on the rule of law, and the decline in the status of law in the country has made it increasingly difficult for the Department to protect its interests.

Encroachment has become widespread only since about 1972. Before that date Forest Department authority was widely respected, many of its senior officers were knowledgable and committed to their jobs, and corruption within the Department was not a major issue. The increase in encroachment after 1972 was presumably partly a result of increasing population pressure, but it is also clear that encroachment often followed a breakdown in the authority of the Forest Department. The earliest serious encroachments were in South Kibale, Kisangi, and Mabira Forests, and in the savanna reserves of the north-west. Some of these were 'official' in the sense that although technically illegal they were encouraged or condoned by Government. In the case of South Kibale and Kisangi it is said that the settlers were misled by the declaration of the Economic War, the Government's call to double agricultural production, and the pronouncement by the President that every Ugandan was free to settle in any part of the country. Taken together, these statements may have been interpreted by some people as *carte blanche* to clear Forest Department land. The encroachment problem appears to have grown much worse since the Libera-

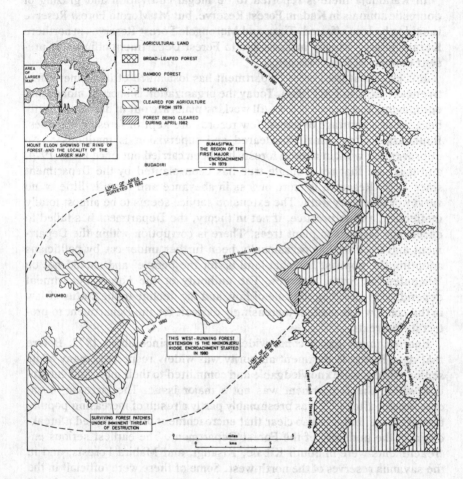

Figure 8. Recent forest destruction on the western slopes of Mt Elgon

Forest distribution on the baseline map as in 1960—the situation in 1978 would have been similar.

tion War, doubtless due to a further decline in Government authority.

When WICO was founded, many Forest Department personnel, including the then Chief Conservator, were moved into the new organization and the feeling is said to have developed that the social standing of WICO was higher than that of the Forest Department. It is now generally alleged that the nationalization of the sawmills encouraged the taking of short-term profits with a great decline in the stringency with which controls over harvesting were applied. For example, given an undersized mahogany tree, the man from the Forest Department who should have prevented felling was placed in a difficult position when a member of WICO argued the economic case for immediate conversion and added, 'Anyway, why should you try and stop me, now that we are all working together as one team?'

A further problem for the Forest Department has been the reduction of its financial support to very low levels since about 1974. This is part of the move towards decreased expenditure on 'services' and increased expenditure on 'security' which has characterized the years since independence. Jorgensen (1981) has calculated the ratio of expenditure on security (army, police, prisons) to that on services (education, health, agriculture, forestry, etc.) for each year between 1901 and 1980. In the early years this ratio was biased heavily in favour of security, but from about 1920 until independence it steadily declined as the Protectorate state expanded its social role. After independence this trend was reversed, the emphasis coming to lie more and more on military expenditure, especially after the coup of 1971; according to Jorgensen (1981) all post-independence governments have 'redistributed resources from non-military sectors to the military'.

Apart from being a financial victim of political instability, forestry has suffered in more immediate ways from politically-related violence. In 1979, during the Liberation War, the Forest Department headquarters at Entebbe were looted and the herbarium cupboards and other valuable items stolen. Military strategy in 1981 and 1982 has led directly to forest clearance in some places, the forests having gained a reputation as likely hiding places for anti-government insurgents. *Eucalyptus* plantations near Masaka, Mbarara, and Iganga towns have been felled for 'security' reasons, and in rural Buganda there has been some general forest and bush clearance, especially in Bulemezi County. Fear of ambush has resulted in the removal of forest and other types of thick vegetation in strips along the sides of roads in some parts of Buganda.

Widespread corruption within the Forest Department is a new factor in Uganda. It should be said immediately that there are many honest, hardworking people within the Department who have battled on against all odds to provide a public service. Nevertheless, there are persistent reports of corruption at all levels within the Service, allegedly involving the use of the

Department for the employees' personal advantage rather than for the public benefit. Corruption takes a number of forms, including the personal acquisition, unauthorized sale, or unauthorized renting of Forest Department land, illegal pit-sawing, illegal sale of timber, collection of bribes to overlook illegality, misuse of Departmental vehicles, and self-allocation of timber allowances exceeding those laid down in regulations. In addition, honest foresters are often inhibited from enforcing regulations because of real or imagined threats of violence; and there can be hesitation in prosecuting those responsible for illegal activities if the honesty of the legal system is itself in doubt. Of all corrupt activities, the most serious from the point of view of the future environment and economy are probably those that result in the transfer of forest land to cultivation. The higher the level of corruption within the Department, the greater its adverse effects on the forest estate are liable to be. This is partly because the direct consequences of malpractices tend to be greater and partly because high-level corruption demoralizes junior staff, making them cynical and disillusioned.

There are several reasons for corruption, but poor supervision, poverty, and an adverse social climate are singled out for mention here. Supervision has declined along with the general fall in professional standards and the increased difficulties of transportation. Regarding poverty, it is no secret that pay levels in the Civil Service are so low that it is virtually impossible for even a senior civil servant to maintain his family without some supplementary support. Civil servants of all government departments are known to spend a considerable part of their working weeks away from their official posts in attempts to scrape together sufficient money to make ends meet. Finally, it is evidence that government organizations are vulnerable during periods of political upheaval; although they may appear to retain their institutional forms intact, they may find it impossible to execute their intended functions to any effect.

Over the past ten years instructions on forestry matters have sometimes been issued over the radio. These announcements sometimes involve major shifts in policy, their legality is sometimes questionable, and their general effectiveness has been low. Examples are as follows:

1973. A prohibition on the burning of grass was declared for the whole of Uganda. The sole exception was Forest Department land in cases where management plans called for an early burn. This announcement had no effect.

1978. (a) Every able-bodied person was instructed to plant a tree. The background to this apparently excellent idea was that the President had heard of the danger of locust invasion from Somalia and had been informed that trees would reduce the threat. The instruction had virtually no effect.

1978. (b) Illegal tree-feeling and charcoal-burning were prohibited in Mabira Forest. There was probably little reduction in illegal activity, but the announcement caused the price of charcoal to jump from 70 to 300—400 shillings per bag.

1981. All pit-sawing in Forest Reserves or on other public land was banned. (This would cover all rural land in Uganda.) This suspension had not been lifted by March 1982, at which time all pit-sawing was presumably illegal. The same announcement also suspended charcoal-burning in Forest Reserves, though permitting it under licence on other public land. (Although there are no figures, it is certain that much of the charcoal burning in Uganda today is unlicensed. One major reason might be the high cost of the licence which each member of a charcoal team is required to purchase and carry. Licences cost 8000 shillings for high forest, 30 000 shillings for plantations, and 20 000 shillings for other land.)

To summarize this chapter, the last ten years have been years of increasing chaos at the national level in Uganda and the effectiveness of the Forest Department has been in decline. Extensive damage to forestry resources has been sustained in a short period of time, and severe shortages of tree products have developed locally.

Chapter 8

The future of forestry

> Tree planting should be elevated above all other activities in most African countries. If the land is densely populated and there is no room for forests let the trees be planted at the borders of each shamba. The care for river beds and catchment areas should be the main topic of all political speeches in all African countries like ours. K. Thairu, *The African Civilization* (the author's country is Kenya)

Taken as a whole, forests cover only a small part of the land surface of Uganda. Visions of vast sweeps of mahogany-rich jungles, such as are entertained by some planners, are quite illusory. Ever since the introduction of agriculture some two thousand five hundred years ago, forests have been cleared to make way for crops and pasture, a process which still continues, so that even the remaining patches of forest are shrinking fast. In savanna and agricultural land trees are also being destroyed. Already there are places which only a few years ago supported a good scattering of woody plants but which today are almost treeless.

Until recently, forest planning was far-sighted and the Forest Department was an effective organization with a high degree of control over its land. All this has changed tremendously during the last ten to fifteen years; forest policy has become short-term and restricted in its aims, all forest working plans are out of date, and many management systems designed to control activities in forest reserves have become ineffective. This weakness of government has contributed to a lack of confidence in government planning, an atmosphere of economic insecurity, and a general fall in community spirit. In turn, these social developments have proved highly detrimental to good forest management, especially as Forest department land and the trees on it represent two of the most readily accessible and valuable resources available for personal acquisition and exploitation by those with sufficient influence.

When considering the future of forestry, it must be stressed that this cannot be discussed without some reference to the wider issues of government organization and population control. In my opinion economic prosperity is most unlikely to be achieved without stabilization of the population. The case for population control is sometimes contested with the argument that the present level and continued increase of the population are ample evidence of the adequacy of natural resources. However, this neglects two factors which assume critical importance when a population approaches the limits of its resources. First, a population which is growing rapidly is liable to reach levels that place excessive demands on the environment, resulting in the destruction of part of the capital of natural resources; this eventually leads to a fall in population. Second, when all resources are fully utilized for immediate consumption, there is no surplus to serve as a buffer against unexpected problems such as periods of drought or social unrest. This may be thought a pessimistic scenario, but it is not fanciful. During 1981, many thousands of people died of starvation in Karamoja, the region of Uganda most susceptible to ecological degradation, and the district has become an internationally recognized disaster area. Given a continuation of present trends, similar tragedies may be expected to occur elsewhere in Uganda, at first probably in other parts of the less resilient north and later in the south.

Some Ugandans regard their country as underpopulated, on the basis of comparison with a country such as Japan, which combines a much higher population density with a much higher standard of living. Japan's economy is heavily industrialized and is sustained in part by importing large quantities of raw materials financed by the export of sophisticated manufactured commodities, as well as by the presence of a social structure particularly well suited to present world economic conditions. It is wishful thinking to suppose that Uganda could follow a similar economic course in the foreseeable future. Development must surely be based overwhelmingly on the exploitation of the natural resources lying within its own borders. If this is true, it is arguable that Uganda is overpopulated even today, since systems of resource management have in practice proved to be incapable of preventing the degradation of some important resources. This is not to suggest that Uganda could not sustain a higher population than the present on a permanent basis, but rather that this can only be achieved by applying stricter controls over the utilization of natural resources.

Attitudes towards family size have proved to be very conservative and, while hoping for voluntary stabilization of the population, it seems probable that in fact the population will go on growing until limited involuntarily, for instance by famine. What should be the reaction of the Forest Department to this prospect? In the shorter term, as I suggest later, there is much that good management by the department can do to help improve the life of the people. But, in the longer term, it is difficult to see how forestry services can avoid being overwhelmed as the number of people relentlessly grows.

The pressure to convert forest reserves into smallholding farms may prove very difficult to resist on a wide front. In view of this prospect I follow Brown (1981) in suggesting that the Department should select a few forests to be conserved intact regardless of pressure. These forests are to serve as reservoirs of genetic resources and examples of natural ecosystems as little disturbed by man as possible. Suitable areas include Bwindi/Kayonza, Kalinzu, Bwamba, Kibale, and Budongo Forests, a list which should not be regarded as exhaustive. As pointed out by Brown (1981), the clearance of such forests is not going to solve the population problem or provide temporary relief on anything but the most minor scale, but their loss would sacrifice biological resources which could be of inestimable value to future generations and which can never be reconstituted once lost.

Turning now to the immediate future of forestry, the first matter to be considered is forest policy, since this provides the rationale for government intervention and defines the spheres of activity of the Forest Department. Present forest policy is not clearly defined: it is an unspecified mixture of the 1971 Forest Policy Statement and an amended version of the policy proposals advanced in the Lockwood Report. The latter document is unhelpful in its statement that forest policy is the sum total of government policies and actions which relate to forests; in the Ugandan context a clear statement of policy is needed to act as a clarion call to help restore a sense of purpose to the Forest Department.

Over the years forest policy has given more and more emphasis to the direct and immediate monetary value of harvesting forest products and less and less to the protective roles of forests. Nicholson (1929) believed that forests and trees should be viewed as components of a wider environment and argued that their value transcends that of the immediate selling price of their wood. For example, he stressed the beneficial effects of trees on climate and advocated a major tree-planting programme to help check the trend towards aridification which he saw could develop as a consequence of widespread tree destruction. The Forest Policy Statement of 1948 shows that by that year government had come to view agriculture and forestry as much as competitors as allies; forestry was assigned the subservient role and the stress was no longer on massive afforestation but on procuring a minimum forest estate. By the time of Lockwood (1973) the interactions of forests and trees with other components of the environment receive hardly a mention. The whole thrust of Lockwood is conceived in immediate financial terms and the protective roles of forests are treated in an off-hand fashion as though they were of little importance. A justification given by Lockwood for this approach is that the financial returns of protective forestry are difficult to assess, which strikes me as an odd argument since the value of protective forestry, as of many other things, is not necessarily related to its ease of measurement.

The gradual shift in forest policy which has occurred over the years has tended to generate an attitude towards forests, among both foresters and the general public, which is exploitative in emphasis and short-term in perspective; no doubt this has contributed to the rapid destruction of forests and trees which is occurring today. In my view Nicholson's arguments were basically correct, and what is needed is a forest policy that recognizes (1) that protective forestry is a central forestry objective, and (2) that forest resources are renewable and should only be utilized at a rate which allows for regeneration. In Uganda there are strong, if not always well understood, links between vegetation, climate, soils, and water resources. The planting of trees, whether as isolated individuals or in well-designed blocks of whatever size, will help to improve the climate for agriculture, cut down the rate of topsoil loss, and ensure adequate supplies of clean water.

It has been accepted for many years that the Forest Department has a role to play on land which is not actually covered by forest or earmarked for the establishment of plantations. Certainly unless great progress is made in managing non-forest vegetation for higher wood yields, especially of firewood, the pressure on the forests themselves will continue to grow. The Forest Department manages extensive areas of non-forest land, generally wooded savanna, and there has been a policy of encouraging the private planting of trees. Both of these activities seem excellent areas of involvement for the Forest Department, which could perhaps be regarded as the official body concerned with tree resources in general. Exactly how trees can best fit into the agricultural landscape must vary from region to region and should be a matter of detailed research. Byaruhanga (1974) has recommended that upper-slope sites in southern Uganda, at present largely unproductive, should be planted with trees such as *Pinus patula*, which is fast-growing and tolerant of poor soils. Actually the planting of trees in farming areas is not only a matter of finding species, sites, and silvicultural techniques which are suitable for each ecological zone; much information is also needed about the influence of local social and economic systems on land-use patterns. In practice Byaruhanga's scheme would have to be implemented largely through private tree-planting, given the way ownership of land is perceived in southern Uganda and in order to supply a suitable financial incentive. In northern Uganda major difficulties in combating deforestation are land-tenure systems which encourage communal ownership of land but individual ownership of livestock. There are major social differences between the various parts of Uganda; therefore a locally based approach is considered essentiall for the success of tree-planting programmes. As will be seen later in this chapter, it is contended that this requires the decentralization of some forestry services.

The Forest Department has been very inadequately financed over recent years. It has been a victim, along with other environmental services, of the increasingly high proportion of government expenditure devoted to security. Presumably a rationalization for this might be that the establishment of governmental authority is a prerequisite for the implementation of systems of environmental control. Unfortunately, however, low expenditure on the environment has contributed to its deterioration, and this in turn must have aggravated social tensions. Clearly a greater financial interest is required in the environment on the part of government. A loud and clear voice in favour of forests and trees, similar to that now heard in Kenya, would greatly assist the work of the Forest Department; so too would a firm commitment by government to the legal position as regards forests.

The effective application of forest policy is very dependent on the existence of a suitable institutional structure. Over the last fifteen years forestry has seen many institutional changes, one example being the return of government to direct involvement in sawmilling. This involvement has proved in practice to be unfortunate and has led to many conflicts of interest between long-term forest management and the sawmill balance sheet. The enforcement of regulations has tended to be waived in favour of quick profit (cf. Jones 1981). My recommendation is to restrict the role of government to regulation, a capacity in which it should be seen to be independent and impartial; no member of the forest service should occupy a position in which he might benefit personally from extractive forestry activities. In view of the latter point, the return of many sawmills to private hands in 1980, while being welcome in itself, is regrettable in that some of the recipients of the sawmills were employed either in the Forest Department or in its associated ministry.

Another case where the institutional structure of forestry should be examined is in respect of the balance of central and local services. In the 1950s and early 1960s, probably the period of maximum effectiveness for forestry, no fewer than four contrasting geographical scales contributed significantly to forestry activities in Uganda. At the village level, local governments were attempting, with varying degrees of success, to cater for every-day wood requirements; nationally, the central Forest Department was looking after larger forests and providing educational and advisory services; regionally, the East African Agricultural and Forestry Research Organisation ran a research centre at Maguga in Kenya, providing wider links within Africa (Pereira 1967a); globally, there were particularly close professional links with the United Kingdom and other British territories. Factors which have contributed to the narrowing of this structure include

the gaining of independence by Uganda, the abolition of local governments, the disintegration of the East African Community, and the failure of
international bodies such as the United Nations agencies to provide very
effective aid. In general, political power has become concentrated at the
national level and the country has become increasingly isolated from the
outside world. It is a defensible thesis that none of the changes in the
administrative structure of forestry has been effected primarily with the
aim of improving forestry services, although it has sometimes been argued
after the event that services had been improved. It seems fair to regard
forestry as at best a passive recipient and at worst a victim of these developments. My view is that the extremely serious environmental degradation
which is occurring in Uganda today calls for a much higher priority to be
given to the requirements of forestry and indeed other environmental
disciplines. The aim of the forestry lobby should be to create institutional
structures which are well suited to the needs of forestry; and, while practical politics might well curtail the extent to which this can be achieved,
nevertheless foresters should make their professional preferences clear to
government.

There is a difference in emphasis between the aims of forestry at the
village level and in the management of large forest reserves. Considering
first the supply of wood to the rural community, the arguments used
several decades ago to justify the decentralization of this sphere of forestry
activities still seem valid today. Communication between the peasant
community and a society of applied scientists such as foresters is beset
with difficulties (*see discussion in* Gluckman 1968). The intermediary most
likely to succeed is the person able to operate through the traditional social
framework; in the context of Uganda, this would predominantly mean the
local man who has received some technical instruction, though not to such
a degree that he has become alienated from his social background. Forestry
is here faced with problems similar to those of the agricultural extension
services (Richards 1969), in which the solution adopted up to the early
1960s was to use established tribal authority as the agent of change. The
approach involved a combination of persuasion and the imposition of rules
(Jorgensen 1981) and a certain amount of success was achieved. After
independence, politicians are said to have wanted to speed up the pace of
agricultural development and the emphasis was now on transformation
rather than improvement. According to Richards (1969) this was the reason
for the replacement of local agricultural services by a centrally based
organization. In agriculture, as in forestry, all the evidence suggests that
present extension arrangements are hopelessly inadequate. My suggestion
is, then, that on the basis of both past performance and theoretical considerations, local forestry services should be returned to local control.

What should be the main activities of local forestry services? Small village-owned forests may seem attractive to some theorists, but are unlikely to serve as a general answer to the problem of rural wood supply. Village forests failed when tried about fifty years ago and in most places would certainly fail again, given the more competitive and individualistic nature of modern Ugandan society. However, small-scale communal projects are worth trying where there is an exceptionally strong feeling of local identity, such as is offered by some schools and churches. Another possible area of action is in the development of small forests owned by the local administration. This was the main activity of the former local forestry services and, judging from previous experience, this could be successful, at least in some parts of Uganda. However, it is the opinion of many informed forestry officers that the main thrust in local forestry work must be the encouragement of tree-planting by private citizens. This is an area where there is tremendous potential for improvement and where the economic and other advantages to the farmer can reveal themselves very quickly. Given locally based forestry services, it should be possible to make rapid strides in this field. A subsidiary advantage could be the creation of a fairly large number of new jobs for foresters.

The aims of management of larger forests are rather specialized and, rather than being placed under local control, they should be administered, as they are now, by a centrally based Forest Department. This department should also be responsible for research and other specialist functions. The reason for keeping larger forests under central control is that, while there are compelling reasons for retaining such forests, their presence is often at variance with the immediate local interest; if administered locally, pressures might well develop which would precipitate their destruction.

Larger blocks of forest should be conserved as part of a general policy of keeping Uganda well wooded, as well as for a number of more specific reasons, some of which are listed below.

The first reason for retaining large forests is to protect catchments. A forest cover on mountains and hills helps to provide a well-regulated supply of water and prevents excessive soil erosion; loss of a forest cover from more rugged terrain could eventually result in an unproductive landscape of bare eroded hills dissected by dry valleys occasionally subject to torrential water flow. Readers who regard this vision as unrealistically alarmist should be warned that this is exactly what has happened extensively in Ethiopia and around the Mediterranean, where once-forested hills have been converted to scrub and bare rock through centuries of forest clearance and soil erosion. Catchment protection alone provides a strong argument for retaining the forest reserves on Mgahinga, Echuya, Bwindi, Rwenzori, and Elgon, as well as on the mountains and hills of Karamoja and elsewhere in northern Uganda. Consideration should also be given to the possibility of creating more catchment forests, especially in the north.

The second reason for conserving large forests is to provide sustained yields of forest products, especially where the quantity or quality required is high. The most important products are high-grade timber, fuel, general-purpose timber (needed in bulk for use in urban centres), and fibre for the manufacture of paper and board. The provision of a sustained supply of high-grade timber has in the past been a principal objective of management in many of the larger forests, such as Budongo, Bugoma, Kalinzu, and Mabira. It is indisputable that the marvellous timbers which can be grown in Uganda will become ever more valuable in a world in which hardwood forests are shrinking fast, and Uganda could generate much foreign currency on a regular basis from this very precious resource. It is to be noted, however, that the value of the timber of some trees which used to be regarded by the Forest Department as weeds has altered greatly since the time when the last working-plans for the natural forests were formulated. Indeed, there is probably no such thing as a weed tree in Uganda today; all wood is valuable and can be sold. In the light of this and in view of the anticipated large internal demand for timber, urgent attention should be given to revising the aims and techniques of management in hardwood forests. My own view is that more emphasis should be given to providing a high yield of general-purpose wood. In regard to the supply of fuel to urban areas, action is needed now to avoid a major impending fuel famine. Mabira and other large forests relatively close to population concentrations should be developed with fuel supply high on the list of priorities. Finally, there is an urgent need to examine, to modify where necessary, and to implement those plans which already exist for the establishment of extensive new plantations to supply pulp for paper and board manufacture.

Further reasons for keeping large forests are the conservation of species and the conservation of examples of ecosystems which have been relatively little modified by man. Species are the product of millions of years of evolution and are irreplaceable if lost through extinction. They provide us with a living inheritance from the past and the loss of species leaves the earth a poorer place for future generations (Kingdon 1973). The economic value of many species for timber is well established; also some tropical-forest herbs and trees are already of great economic value as sources of organic chemicals and materials of all kinds, and tropical forests can be regarded as vast chemical storehouses, as yet little explored (Oldfield 1980; Plotkin and Schultes 1982; Struhsaker 1978). It is widely agreed that the protection of many forest species depends on the conservation of their natural habitat, and this is a strong reason for retaining examples of natural ecosystems unaffected by human disturbance.

The protection of undisturbed forest ecosystems is also of value in itself, for example because they are the only sources of information on the natural functioning of the forests. The elucidation of their workings may lead to discoveries of major economic significance. Examination of nutrient cycling in undisturbed forest ecosystems could help us to devise agricultural systems which are efficient at retaining a soil well stocked with nutrients. It may be recalled that many of the soils of Uganda have their nutrients concentrated in a thin topsoil overlying a virtually sterile subsoil, and that there is great potential for nutrient loss through poor farming practices. Natural forest vegetation represents a biological machine which is extremely efficient at conserving nutrients, and we would greatly benefit if we could determine the mechanisms by which this efficiency is achieved.

One large forest can encompass a range of management objectives or be used only for a single purpose. In discussing the topic of multiple land use, a distinction may be drawn between cases in which a single area of forest is used simultaneously for many purposes and those cases in which a forest is divided into compartments to each of which one objective is assigned. In regard to the former, one of the main questions is the extent to which the harvesting of timber or other forest products may be combined with other objectives (Leggat 1962). Undoubtedly the ideal balance varies greatly from place to place, and accordingly only a few general remarks are given here.

It is inappropriate to try and institute complicated, delicate management systems in the Uganda context; plans should be robust and clearly enforceable, and a drop in potential efficiency should be accepted so that this can be achieved. The taungya system, which incorporates a phase of cultivation in the forest harvesting cycle is a case in point. This system, which has been tried on the northern side of Mt Elgon, allows farmers to enter the forest to clear the ground of tall vegetation and to open temporary farms. The farmers are required to plant young trees from the nursery among their crops and must move off the land when the trees are well established. Ideally, farmers should move through the forest at the same rate as the timber harvesting cycle. Some foresters in Uganda have advocated this system on the grounds that it relieves land pressure and reduces forestry costs, but unfortunately the system can introduce elements that can outweigh possible advantages. The main problems are that topsoil erosion is likely to be much increased and that the added complexity greatly raises the risk of disruption of Forest Department plans. Given the growing land pressure, it is not difficult to conceive of farmers refusing to leave the land at the appointed time and, while the taungya system may theoretically increase efficiency, in practice it is liable to result in an increased workload for foresters and a decrease in environmental quality. The use of the taungya system should not be extended.

Another example where complexity is to be avoided is in connection with the granting of permits to cultivate or graze domestic animals within forest reserves. One danger arising from this practice is illustrated with reference to Mabira Forest, where thousands of temporary farming permits have recently (1982) been granted to farmers who have illegally settled within the forest. Whatever may be the motives of the authorities in issuing the permits, this action is likely to be perceived by the public as a weak, defensive reaction to illegality and in my opinion will probably result in further encroachment.

Where catchment protection is the primary function of a forest, great care must be taken in permitting any additional activities. The advice of McCulloch and Dagg (1962) is that grazing by domestic animals should never be allowed, but that timber harvesting is sometimes acceptable. The principal danger with timber harvesting is topsoil loss, and I suggest that harvesting should be banned completely on rugged mountains such as Rwenzori, on steep slopes wherever they occur, and close to river banks.

Conservation of many forest species is likely to be compatible with timber harvesting, especially if this is by pit-sawing, but some species probably cannot persist in the presence of even fairly low levels of human interference and thus require protection within special nature reserves. In any case, special forest reserves are also needed to conserve examples of little-disturbed forest ecosystems. The breakdown of sawmills during recent years has led to a big increase in pit-sawing, much of which is unlicensed. Some foresters express dismay at the increase in pit-sawing, holding that timber from sawmillers is of a higher quality than that from pit-sawers and that sawmilling is less efficient in terms of waste production. Support for sawmills probably also derives from the greater ease with which sawmills can be regulated. In fact, pit-sawing does have some advantages over sawmilling, notably in providing more jobs, in avoiding much of the disturbance, compaction, and erosion of large areas of topsoil which are associated with sawmilling, and quite likely in allowing a higher sustainable harvest of timber (*see also* Van Orsdol 1983). I am not arguing here that sawmilling should be replaced entirely by pit-sawing—only that the Forest Department should reassess its priorities in this area.

It is long-established forestry policy in Uganda to set aside relatively small areas of land within the larger forests as undisturbed nature reserves, and continuation of this policy is highly desirable, especially for the conservation of samples of forest variation across the country. In addition to these reserves, the Forest Department has recently been creating or intending to create some larger nature reserves, and this too is an excellent idea. Larger reserves not only provide fuller samples of ecosystem variation within a particular geographical locality, but also are more likely to be sufficiently large to maintain viable populations of some forest species which would otherwise not be able to survive. It should be noted in this context that there is considerable uncertainty about the minimum size of reserve needed to maintain viable populations of species, but probably even the largest forest nature reserves proposed for Uganda are too small to protect some larger species of animals. For species conservation it is particularly important to place nature reserves in the species-rich forests of the west, especially Bwindi-Kayonza and Bwamba, but also Kalinzu, Kibale, and Budongo (Hamilton 1981a). Kingdon (1973) has also mentioned Rwenzori and Malabigambo, the latter in Buganda.

If the arguments given in this chapter for conserving larger forests are accepted, it remains to consider which of the surviving large forests should be conserved. Actually, all remaining large forests already lie within forest reserves, they are few in number, and together they constitute only a small fraction of the total land surface of Uganda. In view of their realized and potential value, there can be little doubt that all large forests which are still extant should be retained and that strenuous efforts should be made to evict illegal farmers. Indeed, a strong case can be made for creating new large forests, in order to cater for the huge demand for wood which is predicted for the future.

My conclusion is that a centrally administered Forest Department has a major role to play in Uganda's development. What should be the relationship between the central Forest Department and the proposed locally based forestry administrations? The emphasis in local forestry is on assisting the immediate community and, given the increasing awareness of the tree problem in many parts of the country, my feeling is that local forestry administrations will come to find their services much in demand and the people willing to co-operate in their work. It is vital that forestry officers operating at this level should be readily acceptable to the local society and their education should not involve their withdrawal from the community for long periods of instruction. They do not require a high level of technical education and should be able to draw freely upon information services offered by the central Forest Department. In contrast, it is essential that foresters employed by the central Forest Department develop a professional forestry ethos; this is vital because of the specialized aims of management for the larger forests and because of the likelihood of continuing pressure from local communities to clear large forests for agriculture. The latter force can probably only be restrained effectively by the authority of a Central Government agency with its broader perspectives. It is important that members of the central Forest Department regard themselves as constituting a professional elite with an allegiance first and foremost to the forestry needs of the country as a whole. To achieve this, it is desirable to set pay scales in the central Forest Department at higher levels than in local forestry services, as was the practice when a duel system was formerly in operation. It is suggested that procedures for recruitment and advancement in the central Forest Department should be strictly by ability. Membership of the local community, which is so important as a qualification for local forestry officers engaged in their day-to-day dealings with the public, becomes a minor consideration in the management of large forests for specialist functions. One idea is that all people entering forestry in Uganda, including graduates, should start their careers in local forestry administrations, out of which those with wider interests or who are ambitious can enter the central Forest Department after passing suitable examinations.

Lack of accurate information severely handicaps good forest management in Uganda today (*cf.* Philip 1962). An example discussed in Chapter 7 is the poor state of knowledge concerning the extent and causes of encroachment; another aspect, in this case shared with many other countries (FAO 1982), is the slow progress which has been made in devising silvicultural techniques for tropical forests as sources of timber. The information problem has, therefore, both national and international dimensions. Within Uganda this state of affairs has been exacerbated by the poor maintenance of traditions of scientific and technical expertise relating to forestry and by the low level of contact with forestry communities in other parts of the world during recent years. An example of the former is the tradition of field-based applied ecology pioneered by Eggeling and Dawkins, which has become virtually extinct. Regarding international links, it may be noted that during recent years there has been a very inadequate flow of scientific books and journals into Uganda, and that very few foreign scientists have been working in Uganda's forests.

The problem of lack of information can be regarded as being to a large extent one of maintaining professionalism within small communities of specialized scientists and technicians subject to a high degree of geographical isolation from other similar specialists. Not only are foresters in Uganda intellectually isolated from their forestry comrades elsewhere, but their professionalism is under constant threat of erosion from the pulls of other commitments. These debilitating influences are magnified by the insecure economic and political environment. Much can be achieved through effort at home, but in my opinion strong backing from external scientific and technical communities is required to strengthen professional attitudes, to help restore an atmosphere of confidence, and to keep Ugandans abreast of thinking about forestry in other parts of the world. I regard this as the most desirable objective of 'aid' to forestry, and believe that professional support will be needed for very many years to come, given the social framework in which forestry will have to operate in Uganda.

This view of external assistance differs from that which has prevailed over recent years, during which the main contacts between forestry in Uganda and the outside world have been the despatch of a small number of students for eduction abroad, the occasional participation by senior officers in conferences, and the plugging of perceived gaps in expertise by the temporary recruitment of specialists. The Lockwood Report (1973) is typical of many similar reports on Uganda written during the last twenty years in taking an off-the-peg approach to knowledge; it recommends that foreign experts should be recruited to fulfil particular specialist functions for short contractual periods while training up Ugandan counterparts to take their places. This concept of development assistance, which is one widely found in United Nations bodies, can undoubtedly often be of value, but it can suffer from a number of problems, especially in that it makes little contribution towards providing extended intellectual and psychological support.

My recommendation is that long-term links should be established between the various forestry specialities in Uganda and carefully selected organizations in countries with well-established traditions in applied ecology and forestry. The intention is that people in these foreign bodies should make a long-term commitment to building an understanding of the particular natural and social conditions of Uganda; meanwhile, their Ugandan counterparts will have the opportunity to make reciprocal visits to their sister organizations overseas, and the links have a reasonable chance of leading to a valuable two-way exchange of ideas. The latter is important; aid should not be thought of so much in terms of spreading knowledge from experts to non-experts as in helping provide support for the Uganda experts who are already in place.

Summary and Main Recommendations

1. Every effort should be made to stabilize the size of the population.
2. Forest policy should be revised and widely advertised; the main functions of the Forest Department should be to build up and maintain forest and tree resources and to regulate their use.
3. Neither the Forest Department as an institution nor any of its employees acting privately should be engaged in extractive forest industries.
4. Local forestry services should be established to assist with forestry work at the community level, and particularly to encourage farmers to plant trees.
5. Larger blocks of forest should remain under the control of a centrally organized Forest Department.
6. The Government should vigorously support the work of the Forest Department, financially and otherwise; it should also firmly apply the law as it relates to forests.

7. Research into all aspects of forest ecology and utilization should be vigorously pursued.
8. Long-term links should be forged between the various specialist branches of forestry in Uganda and carefully chosen institutions in countries with well-established scientific traditions.

References

Barry, R. G. and R. J. Chorley (1976). *Atmosphere, Weather and Climate*. 3rd ed. London, Methuen & Co. Ltd.

Begumis, G. B. (1981). Resurrection of coffee smallholdings in Uganda. Proceedings of the Conference on Rural Rehabilitation and Development (A. Nsibambi and J. Katorobo, eds.). Faculty of Social Sciences, Makerere University. pp. 566—95.

Bibangambah, J. S. (1981). An analytical overview of the rural development problem in Uganda. Proceedings of the Conference on Rural Rehabilitation and Development (A. Nsibambi and J. Katorobo, eds.). Faculty of Social Sciences, Makerere University. pp. 10—47.

Bonavia, D. (1981). Flood disaster in China blamed on vanishing forests. *The Times*, 8 September.

Boucher, K. (1975). *Global Climate*. London, English University Press.

Brown, K. W. (1967). *Forest Insects of Uganda. An Annotated List*. Entebbe, Government Printer.

Brown, L. H. (1981). The conservation of forest islands in areas of high human density. *Afr. J. Ecol. 19*: 27—32.

Byaruhanga, T. K. B. (1974). A study of the effect of soil types on the growth and development of *Pinus patula* and *Cupressus lusitanica* under different climatic conditions in Uganda. Unpublished M.Sc. thesis, Makerere University.

Carvalho, J. (1982). A preliminary report on preparation of an inventory of forestry resources using data available at the Nairobi Remote Sensing Facility with reference to Uganda. Manuscript. Forest Research Centre, Kampala.

Caulfield, C. (1982). Where have all the trees gone? *New Scient. 96*: 251.

Charney, J. G. (1975a). Dynamics of deserts and droughts in the Sahel. *Quart. J. R. Met. Soc. 101*: 193—202.

Charney, J. G. (1975b). Drought in the Sahara: A biogeophysical feedback mechanism. *Science 187*: 434—435.

Charney, J. G., P. H. Stone and W. J. Quirk (1976). Drought in the Sahara: Insufficient biogeophysical feedback? *Science 191*: 100—102.

Chenery, E. M. (1960). An introduction to the soils of the Ugandan Protectorate. Kampala, Department of Agriculture, Uganda.

Dawe, M. T. (1906). *A Report on a Botanical Mission through the Forest Districts of Buddu and the Western and Nile Provinces of the Ugandan Protectorate*. London. H.M.S.O.

Dawkins, H. C. (1958). The management of natural tropical high-forest with special reference to Uganda. Imperial Forestry Institute Paper 34, Oxford.

Department of Lands and Surveys (1962). *Atlas of Uganda* (2nd ed. 1967).

Dickinson, R. E. (1980). Effects of tropical deforestation on climate. In *Blowing in the Wind: Deforestation and Long-range Implications*, Studies in Third World Societies 14. Department of Anthropology, College of William and Mary, Williamsburg. pp. 411—441.

Donisthorpe, J. (1959). A pilot study of the mountain gorilla in south-west Uganda. *Uganda J. 23*: 1—28.

Douglass, J. E. (1967). Effects of species and arrangement of forests on evapotranspiration. In *Forest Hydrology* (W. E. Sopper and K. W. Lull, eds.) London, Pergamon Press. pp. 451—61.

Dunne, T. (1979). Sediment yield and land use in tropical catchments. *J. Hydrol.* *42*:281—300.

Earl, D. E. (1968). Latest techniques in the treatment of natural high forest in the South Mengo District. Entebbe, Uganda Forest Department.

Earl, D. E. (1971). The Mabira Forest. *Uganda J.* *35*:90—91.

Eggeling, W. J. (1940). Budongo—an East African mahogany forest. *Emp. For J.* *19*:179—196.

——— (1947). Observations on the ecology of the Budongo rain forest, Uganda. *J. Ecol.* *34*:20—87.

——— (1948a). A review of some vegetational studies in Uganda. *Uganda J.* *12*:139—152.

——— (1948b). Epiphytes in the Budongo Forest. *Uganda J.* *12*:106—114.

Eggeling, W. J. and I. R. Dale (1951). *The Indigenous Trees of the Uganda Protectorate.* (2nd ed.) Entebbe, Government Printer.

FAO (1962). Forest influences. FAO Forestry and Forest Products Studies. Rome.

——— (1967). *Timber Trends and Prospects in Africa.* Rome.

——— (1981). *Les ressources forestières de l'Afrique tropicale.* Rome.

——— (1982). Tropical forest resources (by J.-P. Lanly). FAO Forestry Paper 30. Rome.

Farnworth, E. G. and F. B. Golley (eds) (1974). *Fragile Ecosystems.* Berlin, Springer-Verlag.

Faure, H. (1982). Drought prediction in the Sahel? *Palaeoecol. Afr. 14*:163.

Forest Department (1930). *Annual Report for 1929.* Entebbe, Government Printer.

——— (1934). Uganda timbers. Articles prepared for *Financial Times* Supplement.

——— (1951). A history of the Uganda Forest Department, 1898—1929. Entebbe, Government Printer.

——— (1955). A history of the Uganda Forest Department 1930—1950. Entebbe, Government Printer.

——— (1960). *Annual Report for 1959—1960.*

——— (1964). *Annual Report for 1963—1964.*

——— (1968). *4-year Report for 1964—1968.*

——— (1970). *Departmental Standing Orders* (revised ed.).

——— (1971). *Forestry Policy.* (August)

——— (1974). *Annual Report for 1973—1974.*

Gluckman, M. (1968). Inter-hierarchical roles: Professional and party ethics in tribal areas in South and Central Africa. In *Local-Level Politics* (M. J. Swartz, ed.). London, University of London Press. pp. 69—93.

Golding, D. L. (1970). The effects of forests on precipitation. *For. Chron. 46*:397—402.

Goudie, A. (1981). *The Human Impact.* Oxford, Blackwell.

Government of Uganda (1972). *National Report on the Human Environment.* Prepared for the United Nations Conference on the Human Environment.

Greenway, P. J. (1943). Second draft report on vegetation classification for the approval of the Vegetation Committee, Pasture Research Conference, Nairobi. (Manuscript)

Griffith, G. (1950). Soils and man. *Uganda J. 14*:97—102.

Hamilton, A. C. (1974). Distribution patterns of forest trees in Uganda and their historical significance. *Vegetatio 29*:21—35.

——— (1975). A quantitative analysis of altitudinal zonation in Uganda forests. *Vegetatio 30*:99—106.

——— (1976). The significance of patterns of distribution shown by forest plants and animals in tropical Africa for the reconstruction of Upper Pleistocene palaeoenvironments: A review. *Palaeoecol. Afr. 9*:63—97.

——— (1981a). The Quaternary history of African forests: Its relevance to conservation. *Afr. J. Ecol. 19*:1—6.

——— (1981b). *A Field Guide to Uganda Forest Trees.* Privately published.

——— (1982). Environmental history of East Africa. London and New York, Academic Press.

Harrington, G. N. and I. C. Ross (1974). The savanna ecology of Kidepo Valley National Park. *E. Afr. Wildl. J. 12*:93—105.

Henderson-Sellars, A. (1980). The effect of land clearance and agricultural practices upon climate. In *Blowing in the Wind: Deforestation and Long-range Implications.* Studies in

Third World Societies 14, Department of Anthropology, College of William and Mary, Williamsburg. pp. 443—85.

Hewlett, J. D. (1967). Summary of forests and precipitation session. In *Forest Hydrology* (W. E. Sopper and H. W. Lull, eds). London, Pergamon Press, pp. 241—3.

Hibbert, A. R. (1967). Forest treatment effects on water yield. In *Forest Hydrology* (W. E. Sopper and H. W. Lull, eds). London, Pergamon Press. pp. 527—43.

Hopkins, B. (1962). A trend towards longer dry seasons in south-western Nigeria. *Nature 194* : 861—2.

Hughes, J. F. and Brown, J. R. Lang (1962). The planning and organization of current silvicultural treatments in the Central Forest Reserve of South Mengo District. Paper presented to the 8th Commonwealth Forestry Conference.

Jones, D. B. (1981). Rural rehabilitation and the marketing of agricultural produce. Proceedings of the Conference on Rural Rehabilitation and Development (A. Nsibambi and J. Katorobo, eds). Faculty of Social Sciences, Makerere University. pp. 442—453.

Jorgensen, J. J. (1981). Uganda: A modern History. London, Croom Helm.

Karani, P. (1972). Eucalyptus is here to stay. *Uganda J. 36* : 73—7.

Kendall, R. L. (1969). An ecological history of the Lake Victoria basin. *Ecol. Monogr. 39* : 121—176.

Kew Herbarium (1952 . . .). *Flora of Tropical East Africa.* London, Crown Agents.

Kingdon, J. (1971). *East African Mammals.* Vol. 1. London and New York, Academic Press.

―――― (1973). Endemic mammals and birds in Western Uganda: Measuring Uganda's biological wealth and a plea for supra-economic values. *Uganda J. 37* : 1—7.

Kiregyera, B. (1981). Social-economic data infrastructure and rural development in Uganda. Proceedings of the Conference on Rural Rehabilitation and Development (A. Nsibambi and J. Katorobo eds). Faculty of Social Sciences, Makerere University. pp. 596—620.

Kizito, Z. (1973). Uganda's economic war with regard to sawmilling. *The Woodsman 26* : 22—24.

Langdale-Brown, I. (1960). The vegetation of Uganda (excluding Karamoja). Memoirs, Research Division, Department of Agriculture, ser. 2, no. 6.

Langdale-Brown, I., H. A. Osmaston and J. G. Wilson (1964). *The Vegetation of Uganda and Its Bearing on Land Use.* Entebbe, Government Printer.

Laws, R. M., I. S. C. Parker and R. C. B. Johnstone (1970). Elephants and habitats in North Bunyoro, Uganda. *E. Afr. Wildl. J. 8* : 163—180.

Leggat, G. J. (1962). The reconciliation of forestry and game perservation in Western Uganda. Entebbe, Government Printer.

Lind, E. M. and M. E. S. Morrison (1974). *East African Vegetation.* London, Longman.

Livingstone, D. A. (1967). Postglacial vegetation of the Ruwenzori Mountains in Equatorial Africa. *Ecol. Monogr. 37* : 25—52.

Lockwood Consultants Ltd. (1973). Forest resource development study, Republic of Uganda. Prepared for the Canadian International Development Agency.

McCulloch, J. S. G. and M. Dagg (1962). Hydrological aspects of protection forestry in East Africa. East African Agriculture and Forestry Research Organization. (Manuscript).

McKey, D., P. G. Waterman, C. N. Mbi, J. S. Gartlan and T. T. Struhsaker (1978). Phenolic content of vegetation in two African rain forests: Ecological implications. *Science 202* : 61—64.

McMaster, D. N. (1962). A subsistence crop geography of Uganda. Geographical Publications Ltd.

Milne, G. (1935). Some suggested units of classification and mapping, particularly for East African soils. *Soil Res. 4* : 3.

Morrison, M. E. S. and A. C. Hamilton (1974). Vegetation and climate in the uplands of south-western Uganda during the Later Pleistocene Period, II. Forest clearance and other vegetational changes in the Rukiga Highlands during the past 8000 years. *J. Ecol. 62* : 1—31.

Nicholson, J. W. (1929). The future of forestry in Uganda. Entebbe, Government Printer.

―――― (1930). Note on the influence of forests on climate and water supply in Uganda. Entebbe, Government Printer.

Nsibambi, A. and J. Katorobo (eds) (1981). *Rural Rehabilitation and Development.* Proceedings of a Conference, Faculty of Social Sciences, Makerere University.

Oates, J. F. (1974). The ecology and behaviour of black-and-white colobus monkey (*Colobus guereza* Ruppell) in East Africa. Unpublished Ph.D. thesis, University of London.

Oke, T. R. (1978). Boundary layer climates. London, Methuen & Co.

Oldfield, M. L. (1980). Tropical deforestation and genetic resources conservation. In *Blowing in the Wind: Deforestation and Long-range Implications*. Studies in Third World Societies 14. Department of Anthropology, College of William and Mary, Williamsburg. pp. 277–345.

Osmaston, H. A. (1959). *Working Plan for the Bugoma Forest: 1st Revision Period 1960–1970*. Uganda Forest Department.

Penman, H. L. (1963). *Vegetation and Hydrology*. Commonwealth Agricultural Bureau, England.

Pereira, H. C. (1967a). Forest hydrology research in East and Central Africa. In *Forest Hydrology* (W. E. Sopper and H. W. Lull, eds). London, Pergamon Press, pp. 39–40.

——— (1967b). Effects of land-use on the water and energy budgets of tropical watersheds. In *Forest Hydrology* (W. E. Sopper and H. W. Lull, eds). London, Pergamon Press. pp. 435–50.

Philip, M. S. (1962). *The Management of Tropical High Forest*. Entebbe, Government Printer.

Phillipson, D. W. (1977). *The Later Prehistory of Eastern and Southern Africa*. London Heinemann.

Pierce, R. S. (1967). Evidence of overland flow on forest watersheds. In *Forest Hydrology* (W. E. Sopper and H. W. Lull, eds). London, Pergamon Press. pp. 247–53.

Plotkin, M. J. and R. E. Schultes (1982). Tropical forests as sources of new biodynamic compounds. *Threatened Plants Committee Newsletter 9*:4–5. International Union for Conservation of Nature and Natural Resources, Switzerland.

Potter, G., H. W. Ellsaesser, M. C. MacCracken and F. M. Luther (1975). Possible climatic impact of tropical deforestation. *Nature 258*:697–98.

Richards, A. I. (1969). *The Multi-cultural States of East Africa*. Centre for Developing-Area Studies, McGill University.

Richards, P. W. (1979). *The Tropical Rain Forest*. London, Cambridge University Press.

Ripley, E. A. (1976). Drought in the Sahara: Insufficient biogeophysical feedback? *Science 191*:100.

Rutter, A. J. (1975). The hydrological cycle in vegetation. In *Vegetation and the Atmosphere*, vol. 1 (J. L. Monteith, ed.). London and New York, Academic Press. pp. 111–154.

Sagan, C., O. B. Toon and J. B. Pollack (1979). Anthropogenic albedo changes and the earth's climate. *Science 206*:1363–68.

Sangster, R. G. (1951a). *The Forest Dedication Scheme in Buganda Province*. Entebbe, Government Printer.

——— (1951b). *Buganda Dedication Scheme: Working Plan for Indigenous Forests*. Entebbe, Government Printer.

Street-Perrott, R. A. (1982). Twentieth century fluctuations in lake level in the Ziway-Shala Basin, Ethiopia. *Palaeoecol. Afr. 14*:99–110.

Struhsaker, T. T. (1975). *The Red Colobus Monkey*. Chicago, University of Chicago Press.

——— (1978). Bioeconomic reasons for conserving tropical rain forest. *Recent Adv. Primatology 2*.

——— (1981). Vocalizations, phylogeny and palaeogeography of red colobus monkeys (*Colobus badius*). *Afr. J. Ecol. 19*:265–83.

Synnott, T. J. (1971). Annotated list of the perennial woody vegetation of the West Ankole forests. *Uganda J. 35*:1–12.

——— (1975). Factors affecting the regeneration and growth of seedlings of *Entandrophragma utile* (Dawe & Sprague) Sprague. Unpublished Ph.D. thesis, Makerere University.

Tack, C. H. (1969). *Uganda Timbers*. Entebbe, Government Printer.

Thairu, K. (1975). *The African Civilization*. Nairobi, East African Literature Bureau.

Thomas, A. S. (1941). The vegetation of the Sese Islands, Uganda: An illustration of edaphic factors in tropical ecology. *J. Ecol. 29*:330–53.

Thomas, A. S. (1943). The vegetation of the Karamoja District, Uganda. *J. Ecol. 31*:149–177.

Troup, R. S. (1922). *Forestry in Uganda.* London, Crown Agents.

Uganda Gazette Supplement (1948). Forest Policy. Announced by H. E. the Governor. (Issued 15 June).

Uganda J. 12 : 173—5 (1948). The toll of sleeping sickness.

UNESCO (1964). *African Timber Trends and Prospects.*

USAID (1982). *Uganda Agricultural Sector Assessment.* Washington.

Van Orsdol, K. G. (1983). The status of Kibale Forest Reserve in Western Uganda and recommendations for its conservation and management. Report prepared for the Ministry of Agriculture and Forestry and other bodies.

van Someren, V. G. L. and G. R. C. van Someren (1949). The birds of Bwamba. *Uganda J. 13* (suppl.).

Wilson, J. G. (1962). *The Vegetation of Karamoja District.* Uganda Department of Agriculture.

Wood, C. A. and R. R. Lovett (1974). Drought and the solar cycle. *Nature 251* : 594—96.

Zinke, P. J. (1967). Forest interception studies in the United States. In *Forest Hydrology* (W. E. Sopper and H. W. Lull, eds). New York, Pergamon Press.

Index